BIG IDEAS
MATH.

Skills Review Handbook

BIG IDEAS
LEARNING.

Erie, Pennsylvania
BigIdeasLearning.com

Big Ideas Learning, LLC
1762 Norcross Road
Erie, PA 16510-3838
USA

For product information and customer support, contact Big Ideas Learning
at **1-877-552-7766** or visit us at ***BigIdeasLearning.com***.

Cover credit: Kisa-Murisa/iStock/Getty Images Plus

Printed in the U.S.A.

ISBN 13: 978-1-64208-015-5

1 2 3 4 5 6 7 8 9-22 21 20 19 18

Skills Review Handbook

The Skills Review Handbook provides examples and practice to review concepts from earlier grades. This book can be used for remediation, enrichment, and differentiation.

PRACTICE MAKES PURR-FECT®

I remember things when I practice.

Contents

REVIEW: Whole Number Place Value

Name _____

Key Concept and Vocabulary

Thousands	Hundreds	Tens	Ones
1,	2	4	5

1,000	200	40	5

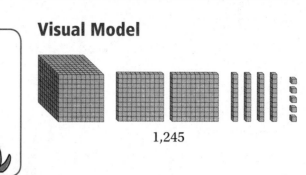

Place Value

Visual Model

1,245

Skill Examples

1. The value of the digit 5 in 357 is 50.

2. The value of the digit 8 in 4,318 is 8.

3. The value of the digit 6 in 625 is 600.

4. The value of the digit 2 in 2,743 is 2,000.

5. The value of the digit 0 in 8,024 is 0.

Application Example

6. A game console costs $345. A video game costs $39. Which price has a 3 in the tens place?

	Hundreds	Tens	Ones
Game console	3	4	5
Video game		3	9

∴ The price of the video game has a 3 in the tens place.

PRACTICE MAKES *PURR*-FECT®

Check your answers at BigIdeasMath.com.

Write the value of the underlined digit.

7. 6̲7 _____

8. 1̲9 _____

9. 2̲78 _____

10. 52̲1 _____

11. 33̲6 _____

12. 1,7̲98 _____

13. 94̲0 _____

14. 6̲,490 _____

15. 2,5̲23 _____

16. 8,1̲46 _____

17. 7,0̲25 _____

18. 4,34̲4 _____

Write the number shown by the model.

19. _____

20. _____

Write and compare the values of the underlined digits.

21. 6̲,582 and 5̲,682

22. 9,7̲41 and 4̲17

23. 2,5̲76 and 4,5̲80

24. 23̲3 and 8,33̲2

___ ☐ ___   ___ ☐ ___   ___ ☐ ___   ___ ☐ ___

25. **BUCKET TOSS** You toss 3 balls into a blue bucket, 2 balls into a red bucket, and 4 balls into a yellow bucket. You score 243 points. How many points is one ball worth in each bucket: 1, 10, or 100 points? Explain. _____

_____

REVIEW: Writing Number Forms

Name _____

Key Concept and Vocabulary

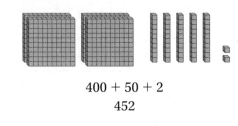

Standard form: 452

Expanded form: 400 + 50 + 2

Word form: four hundred fifty-two

Visual Model

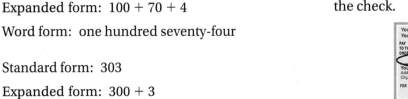

400 + 50 + 2

452

Skill Examples

1. Standard form: 174

   Expanded form: 100 + 70 + 4

   Word form: one hundred seventy-four

2. Standard form: 303

   Expanded form: 300 + 3

   Word form: three hundred three

Application Example

3. Use the number 200 + 90 + 7 to complete the check.

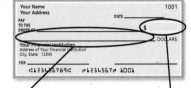

   two hundred ninety-seven, $297

PRACTICE MAKES *PURR*-FECT®

Check your answers at BigIdeasMath.com.

Write the number in two other forms.

4. Standard form: 135

   Expanded form: _____

   Word form: _____

5. Standard form: 760

   Expanded form: _____

   Word form: _____

6. Standard form: _____

   Expanded form: 800 + 50 + 4

   Word form: _____

7. Standard form: _____

   Expanded form: 400 + 2

   Word form: _____

8. Standard form: _____

   Expanded form: _____

   Word form: six hundred thirty-three

9. Standard form: _____

   Expanded form: _____

   Word form: three hundred nineteen

WRITE A CHECK Use the number to complete the check.

10. 100 + 20 + 1

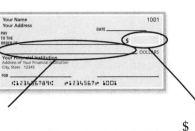

_____ $_____

11. 200 + 40

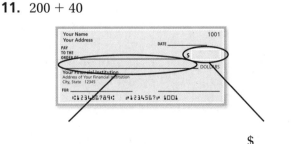

_____ $_____

REVIEW: Writing Number Forms of Multi-Digit Numbers

Key Concept and Vocabulary

Thousands Period			Ones Period		
Hundreds	**Tens**	**Ones**	**Hundreds**	**Tens**	**Ones**
8	7	1,	2	9	3

Standard form: 871,293

Expanded form: $800,000 + 70,000 + 1,000 + 200 + 90 + 3$

Word form: eight hundred seventy-one thousand, two hundred ninety-three

Number forms

Skill Examples

1. Standard form: 90,625

   Expanded form: $90,000 + 600 + 20 + 5$

   Word form: ninety thousand,
   six hundred twenty-five

2. Standard form: 203,011

   Expanded form: $200,000 + 3,000 + 10 + 1$

   Word form: two hundred three thousand,
   eleven

PRACTICE MAKES *PURR*-FECT®

Check your answers at BigIdeasMath.com.

Write the number in two other forms.

3. Standard form: 52,987

   Expanded form: _____

   Word form: _____

4. Standard form: _____

   Expanded form: $700,000 + 10,000 + 3,000 + 600 + 6$

   Word form: _____

5. Standard form: _____

   Expanded form: _____

   Word form: one hundred five thousand, ninety-nine

6. Complete the table.

Standard form	Word Form	Expanded Form
	eight thousand, seven hundred forty-one	
		$30,000 + 9,000 + 500 + 20$
	fifteen thousand, four hundred four	
612,010		

Skills Review Topic 1.3 3

Name _____

Key Concept and Vocabulary

is less than   is greater than

$432 < 436$ $439 > 436$

$436 = 436$

is equal to

Comparing

Visual Model

432 433 434 435 436 437 438 439

less than 436 | greater than 436

Skill Examples

1. $81 > 54$
2. $17 < 32$
3. $63 < 65$
4. $90 = 90$
5. $737 > 568$
6. $326 > 316$
7. $159 < 259$
8. $842 < 843$

Application Example

9. There are 498 pages in a math book. There are 536 pages in a science book. Which book has more pages?

$498 < 536$

The science book has more pages.

PRACTICE MAKES PURR-FECT®

Check your answers at BigIdeasMath.com.

Compare.

10. 42 ☐ 70
11. 68 ☐ 64
12. 326 ☐ 285
13. 421 ☐ 546

14. 915 ☐ 907
15. 592 ☐ 594
16. 112 ☐ 112
17. 397 ☐ 793

18. 272 ☐ 227
19. 789 ☐ 879
20. 630 ☐ 63
21. 104 ☐ 100 + 40

Graph the numbers on the number line. Then order the numbers from least to greatest.

22. 712, 720, 710 _____

23. 445, 444, 450 _____

710 711 712 713 714 715 716 717 718 719 720

440 441 442 443 444 445 446 447 448 449 450

Order the lengths from shortest to longest.

24. 354 cm, 365 cm, 343 cm, 356 cm

25. 932 cm, 924 cm, 943 cm, 934 cm

_____

_____

26. **VIDEO GAME** You score 566 points in a video game. Your friend scores 655 points in a video game. Who scores more points?_____

27. **PUZZLE PIECES** You put together 78 pieces of a 100-piece puzzle. Your friend puts together 48 pieces of a 75-piece puzzle. Who has few puzzle pieces left to put together? _____

REVIEW: Comparing Multi-Digit Whole Numbers

Name _____

Key Concept and Vocabulary

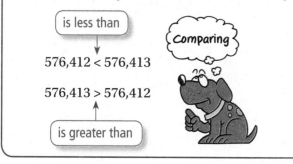

is less than

576,412 < 576,413

576,413 > 576,412

is greater than

Comparing

Visual Model

Thousands Period			Ones Period		
Hundreds	Tens	Ones	Hundreds	Tens	Ones
5	7	6,	4	1	2
5	7	6,	4	1	3

Skill Examples

1. 6,489 > 6,429

2. 83,563 < 87,356

3. 296,872 > 296,472

4. 105,834 < 125,834

Application Example

5. According to a recent U.S. Census, the population of Pittsburgh, PA, is 305,704 and the population of Corpus Christi, TX, is 305,215. Which city has a greater population?

   305,704 > 305,215

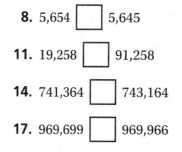

Pittsburgh, PA, has a greater population.

PRACTICE MAKES PURR-FECT®

Check your answers at BigIdeasMath.com.

Compare.

6. 2,584 ☐ 2,854

7. 67,392 ☐ 61,392

8. 5,654 ☐ 5,645

9. 33,783 ☐ 33,782

10. 904,512 ☐ 904,612

11. 19,258 ☐ 91,258

12. 456,789 ☐ 456,780

13. 359,922 ☐ 259,922

14. 741,364 ☐ 743,164

15. 626,846 ☐ 62,684

16. 86,123 ☐ 86,132

17. 969,699 ☐ 969,966

18. seven hundred six thousand, ninety-five ☐ 760,095

19. 118,540 ☐ eighteen thousand, five hundred forty

20. three thousand, seven hundred thirty-three ☐ 373,300

21. **ATTENDANCE** A football team's yearly attendance was 588,942. A hockey team's yearly attendance was 528,946. Which team had a greater yearly attendance?

_____

22. **PINBALL** The high score of a pinball game is 346,923. You score 364,239 points. Your friend scores 346,293 points. Did either of you beat the high score?

REVIEW: Rounding Whole Numbers

Name _____

Key Concept and Vocabulary

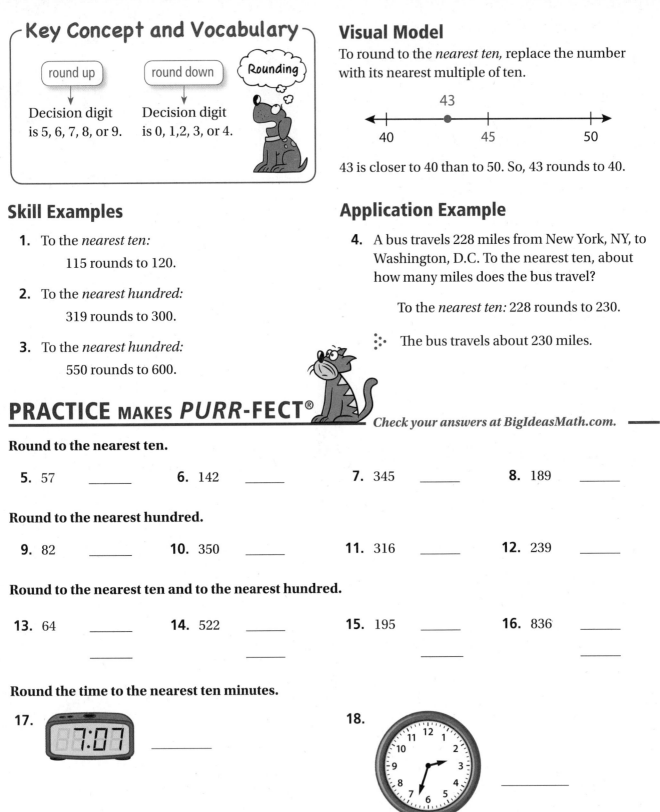

round up
↓
Decision digit
is 5, 6, 7, 8, or 9.

round down
↓
Decision digit
is 0, 1, 2, 3, or 4.

Rounding

Visual Model

To round to the *nearest ten,* replace the number with its nearest multiple of ten.

43

40   45   50

43 is closer to 40 than to 50. So, 43 rounds to 40.

Skill Examples

1. To the *nearest ten:*

   115 rounds to 120.

2. To the *nearest hundred:*

   319 rounds to 300.

3. To the *nearest hundred:*

   550 rounds to 600.

Application Example

4. A bus travels 228 miles from New York, NY, to Washington, D.C. To the nearest ten, about how many miles does the bus travel?

   To the *nearest ten:* 228 rounds to 230.

   ∴ The bus travels about 230 miles.

PRACTICE MAKES *PURR*-FECT®

Check your answers at BigIdeasMath.com.

Round to the nearest ten.

5. 57 _____

6. 142 _____

7. 345 _____

8. 189 _____

Round to the nearest hundred.

9. 82 _____

10. 350 _____

11. 316 _____

12. 239 _____

Round to the nearest ten and to the nearest hundred.

13. 64 _____

14. 522 _____

15. 195 _____

16. 836 _____

_____   _____   _____   _____

Round the time to the nearest ten minutes.

17. `7:07` _____

18. _____

19. **STUDENT POPULATION** There are 879 students at a school. To the nearest hundred, about how many students are at the school? _____

20. **LAPTOP PRICE** A laptop costs about $700. Describe the actual price of the laptop.

_____

REVIEW: Rounding Multi-Digit Whole Numbers

Name _____

Key Concept and Vocabulary

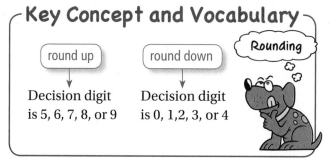

round up → Decision digit is 5, 6, 7, 8, or 9

round down → Decision digit is 0, 1, 2, 3, or 4

Rounding

Visual Model

Round to the *nearest thousand*.

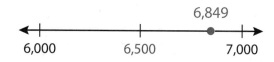

6,849 is closer to 7,000 than to 6,000.
So, 6,849 rounds to 7,000.

Skill Examples

1. To the *nearest thousand*:
   11,486 rounds to 11,000.

2. To the *nearest ten thousand*:
   286,219 rounds to 290,000.

3. To the *nearest hundred thousand*:
   750,671 rounds to 800,000.

Application Example

4. 621,597 people vote in an election. To the nearest ten thousand, about how many people vote in the election?

   To the *nearest ten thousand*:
   621,597 rounds to 620,000.

   ∴ About 620,000 people vote in the election.

PRACTICE MAKES *PURR*-FECT®

Check your answers at BigIdeasMath.com.

Round to the nearest thousand.

5. 3,923 _____   6. 83,682 _____   7. 454,258 _____   8. 536 _____

Round to the nearest ten thousand.

9. 54,732 _____   10. 317,360 _____   11. 892,583 _____   12. 8,579 _____

Round to the nearest hundred thousand.

13. 112,004 _____   14. 535,287 _____   15. 251,840 _____   16. 73,916 _____

Round ★ to the nearest thousand and to the nearest ten thousand.

17.
86,000   86,500   87,000

Nearest thousand: _____

Nearest ten thousand: _____

18.
53,000   53,500   54,000

Nearest thousand: _____

Nearest ten thousand: _____

19. **MOUNT EVEREST** Mount Everest is 8,848 meters tall. To the nearest thousand, about how tall is Mount Everest? _____

20. **CAR PRICE** A new car costs about $20,000. Describe the actual price of the car.

_____

REVIEW: Adding within 100

Name _____

Key Concept and Vocabulary

sum

$8 + 5 = 13$

addends

Add.

Visual Model

To add on a number line, move to the *right*.

$34 + 12 = 46$

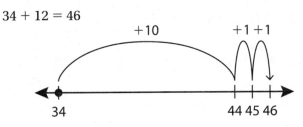

$+10$ $+1$ $+1$

34   44 45 46

Skill Examples

1.
$$\begin{array}{r} 1 \\ 56 \\ + 26 \\ \hline 82 \end{array}$$

2.
$$\begin{array}{r} 1 \\ 32 \\ 11 \\ + 27 \\ \hline 70 \end{array}$$

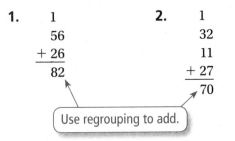

Use regrouping to add.

3. $62 + \ 19 = ?$
$$\quad\ -1 \quad +1$$
$$61 + \ 20 = 81$$

Use compensation to add.

So, $62 + 19 = 81$.

Application Example

4. You have 54 tickets and win 17 more. How many tickets do you have in all?

$$\begin{array}{r} 1 \\ 54 \\ + 17 \\ \hline 71 \end{array}$$

You have 71 tickets in all.

PRACTICE MAKES *PURR-FECT*®

Check your answers at BigIdeasMath.com. ▬

Find the sum.

5. $60 + 20 =$ _____

6. $40 + 50 =$ _____

7. $45 + 30 =$ _____

8. $21 + 60 =$ _____

9.
$$\begin{array}{r} 81 \\ + 17 \\ \hline \end{array}$$

10.
$$\begin{array}{r} 54 \\ + 13 \\ \hline \end{array}$$

11.
$$\begin{array}{r} 25 \\ 13 \\ + 41 \\ \hline \end{array}$$

12.
$$\begin{array}{r} 52 \\ 14 \\ + 16 \\ \hline \end{array}$$

13. $76 + 19 =$ _____

14. $39 + 8 =$ _____

15. $14 + 36 + 24 =$ _____

16. $33 + 38 + 26 =$ _____

17. VIDEO GAME You collect 73 coins in Level 1 and 14 coins in Level 2 of a video game. How many coins do you collect in all? _____

18. SHOPPING TRIP A board game costs $15, a card game costs $14, and a puzzle costs $17. You buy all of the items. How much money do you spend? _____

19. COLLECTING SEASHELLS You have 6 seashells and find 9 more. Your friend has 48 seashells. How many seashells do you and your friend have in all? _____

REVIEW: Adding within 1,000

Name _____

Key Concept and Vocabulary

```
     1
   126 ◄── addends
 + 325 ◄──
   451 ◄── sum
```

Add.

Visual Model

To add on a number line, move to the *right*.

$486 + 212 = 698$

```
      +100    +100    +10 +1 +1
    486      586      686  696 697 698
```

Skill Examples

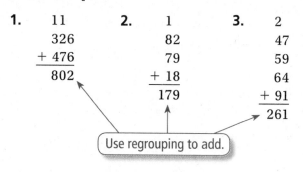

1.
```
    11
   326
 + 476
   802
```

2.
```
     1
    82
    79
  + 18
   179
```

3.
```
     2
    47
    59
    64
  + 91
   261
```

Use regrouping to add.

4. $197 + 448 = ?$
```
  +  3    -  3
  200 +  445 = 645
```

Use compensation to add.

So, $197 + 448 = 645$.

Application Example

5. 214 second-grade students and 209 third-grade students vote in a school election. How many students vote in all?

```
     1
   214
 + 209
   423
```

423 students vote in all.

PRACTICE MAKES *PURR-FECT*®

Check your answers at BigIdeasMath.com.

Find the sum.

6.
```
   432
 + 524
```

7.
```
   748
 + 193
```

8.
```
    81
    65
 +  17
```

9.
```
    26
    52
     5
 +  98
```

10. $158 + 100 = $ _____

11. $316 + 10 = $ _____

12. $627 + 259 = $ _____

13. $416 + 294 = $ _____

14. $793 + 108 = $ _____

15. $267 + 585 = $ _____

16. $247 + 374 = $ _____

17. $31 + 63 + 89 = $ _____

18. MUSIC You have 375 songs on your tablet. You download 192 more. How many songs are on your tablet now? _____

19. NUMBER LINE Write the equation shown by the number line.

_____

```
      +100    +100    +100    +1 +1 +1 +1
    524     624     724     824 825 826 827 828
```

REVIEW: Subtracting within 100

Name _____

Key Concept and Vocabulary

difference

$16 - 6 = 10$

Subtract.

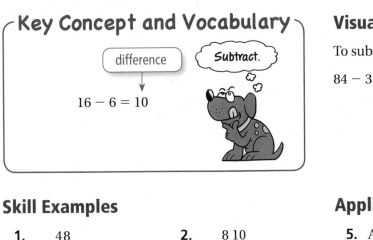

Visual Model

To subtract on a number line, move to the *left*.

$84 - 31 = 53$

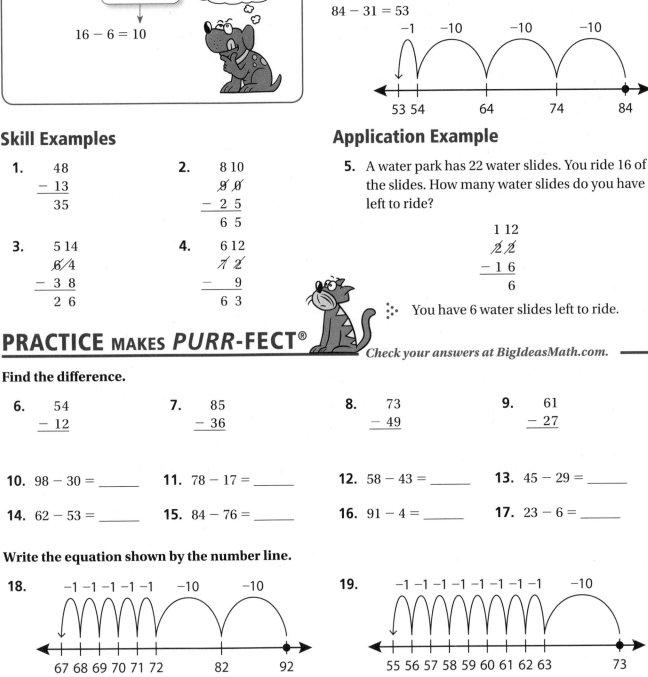

Skill Examples

1. $\begin{array}{r} 48 \\ -\ 13 \\ \hline 35 \end{array}$

2. $\begin{array}{r} 8\ 10 \\ \cancel{9}\ \cancel{0} \\ -\ 2\ 5 \\ \hline 6\ 5 \end{array}$

3. $\begin{array}{r} 5\ 14 \\ \cancel{6}\diagup 4 \\ -\ 3\ 8 \\ \hline 2\ 6 \end{array}$

4. $\begin{array}{r} 6\ 12 \\ \cancel{7}\ \cancel{2} \\ -\ \ \ 9 \\ \hline 6\ 3 \end{array}$

Application Example

5. A water park has 22 water slides. You ride 16 of the slides. How many water slides do you have left to ride?

$\begin{array}{r} 1\ 12 \\ \cancel{2}\ \cancel{2} \\ -\ 1\ 6 \\ \hline 6 \end{array}$

You have 6 water slides left to ride.

PRACTICE MAKES PURR-FECT®

Check your answers at BigIdeasMath.com.

Find the difference.

6. $\begin{array}{r} 54 \\ -\ 12 \\ \hline \end{array}$

7. $\begin{array}{r} 85 \\ -\ 36 \\ \hline \end{array}$

8. $\begin{array}{r} 73 \\ -\ 49 \\ \hline \end{array}$

9. $\begin{array}{r} 61 \\ -\ 27 \\ \hline \end{array}$

10. $98 - 30 =$ _____

11. $78 - 17 =$ _____

12. $58 - 43 =$ _____

13. $45 - 29 =$ _____

14. $62 - 53 =$ _____

15. $84 - 76 =$ _____

16. $91 - 4 =$ _____

17. $23 - 6 =$ _____

Write the equation shown by the number line.

18.

_____

19.

_____

20. **TALENT SHOW** A talent show has 54 acts. 36 acts perform. How many acts still have to perform? _____

21. **CRAFT FAIR** Descartes takes 88 bracelets to a craft fair. He sells 6 bracelets the first day and 24 bracelets the second day. How many bracelets does he have left to sell?

_____

REVIEW: Subtracting within 1,000

Name _____

Key Concept and Vocabulary

$$\begin{array}{r} 8\,4\,6 \\ -\ 7\,2\,3 \\ \hline 1\,2\,3 \end{array}$$ ← difference

Subtract.

Visual Model

To subtract on a number line, move to the *left*.

$426 - 113 = 313$

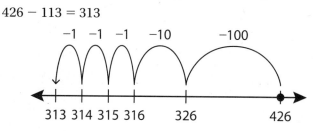

Skill Examples

1.
$$\begin{array}{r} 5\,9\,7 \\ -\ 2\,3\,1 \\ \hline 3\,6\,6 \end{array}$$

2.
$$\begin{array}{r} 5\ \ 15 \\ \cancel{6}\,\cancel{5}\,8 \\ -\ 1\,7\,4 \\ \hline 4\,8\,4 \end{array}$$

3.
$$\begin{array}{r} 13 \\ 8\,\cancel{3}\,15 \\ \cancel{9}\,\cancel{4}\,\cancel{5} \\ -\ 3\,6\,9 \\ \hline 5\,7\,6 \end{array}$$

4.
$$\begin{array}{r} 9 \\ 5\ 10\,10 \\ \cancel{6}\,\cancel{0}\,\cancel{0} \\ -\ 4\,8\,2 \\ \hline 1\,1\,8 \end{array}$$

Application Example

5. Newton sends 327 text messages in a month. Descartes sends 218 text messages. How many more text messages does Newton send than Descartes?

$$\begin{array}{r} 1\ \ 17 \\ \cancel{2}\,\cancel{7} \\ 3\,2\,7 \\ -\ 2\,1\,8 \\ \hline 1\,0\,9 \end{array}$$

Newton sends 109 more text message than Descartes.

PRACTICE MAKES PURR-FECT®

Check your answers at BigIdeasMath.com.

Find the difference.

6.
$$\begin{array}{r} 6\,5\,7 \\ -\ 1\,3\,6 \end{array}$$

7.
$$\begin{array}{r} 4\,1\,4 \\ -\ 3\,4\,2 \end{array}$$

8.
$$\begin{array}{r} 9\,2\,1 \\ -\ 5\,6\,3 \end{array}$$

9.
$$\begin{array}{r} 7\,0\,0 \\ -\ 2\,9\,5 \end{array}$$

10. $805 - 100 = $ _____

11. $297 - 10 = $ _____

12. $879 - 380 = $ _____

13. $926 - 618 = $ _____

14. $712 - 239 = $ _____

15. $943 - 156 = $ _____

16. $500 - 142 = $ _____

17. $401 - 368 = $ _____

18. FOOD DRIVE Your class collects 285 cans for a food drive. Your friend's class collects 179 cans. How many more cans does your class collect than your friend's class? _____

19. ANIMAL WEIGHTS A gorilla weighs 476 pounds. A leopard weighs 308 pounds less than the gorilla. How much does the leopard weigh? _____

20. NUMBER LINE Write the equation shown by the number line.

_____

21. ARCADE You have 400 tokens. You spend 126 tokens before lunch and 148 tokens after lunch. How many tokens do you have left? _____

REVIEW: Adding and Subtracting Multi-Digit Numbers

Name _____

Key Concept and Vocabulary

$$18,416 + 1,562 = 19,978$$

$$75,938 - 2,415 = 73,523$$

Add and subtract.

Use place value to line up the numbers.

Visual Model

To add on a number line, move to the *right*.

$40,651 + 20,300 = 60,951$

$+20,000$ $+300$

40,651   60,651 60,951

To subtract on a number line, move to the *left*.

Skill Examples

1.
$$\begin{array}{r} 1\,1 \\ 10,326 \\ +\ 22,487 \\ \hline 32,813 \end{array}$$

2.
$$\begin{array}{r} 1\ \ 11 \\ 386,159 \\ +541,372 \\ \hline 927,531 \end{array}$$

3.
$$\begin{array}{r} 6\,10\ \ 7\,14 \\ 7\not0\,4,\not8\not4\,6 \\ -\ 413,751 \\ \hline 291,095 \end{array}$$

4.
$$\begin{array}{r} 9 \\ 1\,10\,11 \\ 97,\not2\not0\not1 \\ -\ 63,164 \\ \hline 34,037 \end{array}$$

Application Example

5. A video receives 9,720 views the first day and 32,583 views the second day. How many views does the video receive in two days?

$$\begin{array}{r} 1\,1\ \ 1 \\ 32,583 \\ +\ 9,720 \\ \hline 42,303 \end{array}$$

⋮⋮ The video receives 42,303 views in two days.

PRACTICE MAKES *PURR-FECT*®

Check your answers at BigIdeasMath.com. —

Find the sum or difference.

6.
$$\begin{array}{r} 153,619 \\ +\ 413,751 \\ \hline \end{array}$$

7.
$$\begin{array}{r} 75,218 \\ -\ 51,914 \\ \hline \end{array}$$

8.
$$\begin{array}{r} 890,126 \\ -\ 3,450 \\ \hline \end{array}$$

9. $6,387 + 7,935 =$ _____

10. $40,524 + 19,488 =$ _____

11. $671,837 + 5,949 =$ _____

12. $4,973 - 1,215 =$ _____

13. $973,684 - 529,810 =$ _____

14. $256,349 - 82,157 =$ _____

Write the equation shown by the number line.

15. $+3,000$ $+400$ $+60$

4,215   7,215   7,615 7,675

_____

16. -200 $-6,000$ $-100,000$

20,348 20,548   26,548   126,548

_____

17. **ATTENDANCE** 92,721 fans attend the first football game of the season. 90,418 fans attend the second game. How many total fans attend the two football games? _____

REVIEW: Estimating Whole Number Sums and Differences

Name _____

Key Concept and Vocabulary

$$
\begin{array}{r}
71 \\
+\ 26 \\
\end{array}
\rightarrow
\begin{array}{r}
70 \\
+\ 30 \\
\hline
100
\end{array}
$$

Round to the nearest ten.

Estimate.

$$
\begin{array}{r}
832 \\
-\ 478 \\
\end{array}
\rightarrow
\begin{array}{r}
800 \\
-\ 500 \\
\hline
300
\end{array}
$$

Round to the nearest hundred.

Visual Model

close to 150

153

```
|←———•———|———————|———→|
  150    155    160
```

close to 350

348

```
|←———————|———•———|———→|
  340    345    350
```

153 + 348 is about 500.

Skill Examples

1. Round to the nearest hundred to estimate the sum.

$$
\begin{array}{r}
628 \\
+\ 283 \\
\end{array}
\rightarrow
\begin{array}{r}
600 \\
+\ 300 \\
\hline
900
\end{array}
$$

So, 628 + 283 is about 900.

2. Use compatible numbers to estimate the difference.

$$
\begin{array}{r}
557 \\
-\ 21 \\
\end{array}
\rightarrow
\begin{array}{r}
550 \\
-\ 25 \\
\hline
525
\end{array}
$$

So, 557 − 21 is about 525.

Application Example

3. A beach hut owner sells 178 towels and 54 pairs of goggles. About how many items does the owner sell?

Use compatible numbers to estimate the sum.

$$
\begin{array}{r}
178 \\
+\ 54 \\
\end{array}
\rightarrow
\begin{array}{r}
175 \\
+\ 50 \\
\hline
225
\end{array}
$$

The owner sells about 225 items.

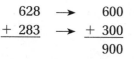

PRACTICE MAKES *PURR*-FECT®

Check your answers at BigIdeasMath.com.

Round to the nearest ten to estimate the sum or difference.

4. 62 + 16 is about _____.   **5.** 894 − 435 is about _____.   **6.** 944 − 29 is about _____.

Round to the nearest hundred to estimate the sum or difference.

7. 163 + 481 is about _____.   **8.** 245 + 86 is about _____.   **9.** 754 − 372 is about _____.

Use compatible numbers to estimate the sum or difference.

10. 524 + 347 is about _____.   **11.** 926 − 628 is about _____.   **12.** 773 − 28 is about _____.

13. **WATER BALLOONS** You fill 153 water balloons. Your friend fills 209 water balloons. About how many water balloons do you and your friend fill? _____

14. **TRADING CARDS** You have 118 fire animal cards and 147 water animal cards. About how many more water animal cards do you have than fire animal cards? _____

15. **TICKETS** You sell 351 raffle tickets. Newton sells 216 tickets and Descartes sells 184 tickets. About how many tickets do you, Newton, and Descartes sell in all? _____

REVIEW: Equal Groups and Multiplication

Name _____

Key Concept and Vocabulary

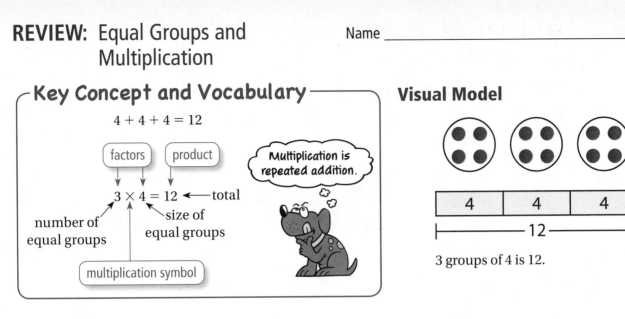

$4 + 4 + 4 = 12$

factors   product

$3 \times 4 = 12$ ← total

number of equal groups

size of equal groups

multiplication symbol

Multiplication is repeated addition.

Visual Model

3 groups of 4 is 12.

Skill Examples

1.

2 groups of 5
$5 + 5 = 10$
$2 \times 5 = 10$

2.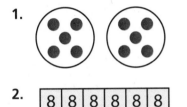

6 groups of 8
$8 + 8 + 8 + 8 + 8 + 8 = 48$
$6 \times 8 = 48$

Application Example

3. You have 4 boxes. There are 7 stuffed animals in each box. How many stuffed animals are there in all?

$7 + 7 + 7 + 7 = 28$
$4 \times 7 = 28$

∴ There are 28 stuffed animals.

PRACTICE MAKES *PURR-FECT*®

Check your answers at BigIdeasMath.com.

Use the model to complete the statements.

4.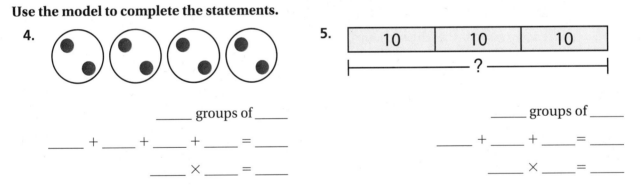

_____ groups of _____

_____ + _____ + _____ + _____ = _____

_____ × _____ = _____

5.

| 10 | 10 | 10 |

?

_____ groups of _____

_____ + _____ + _____ = _____

_____ × _____ = _____

Write the addition equation as a multiplication equation.

6. $5 + 5 + 5 + 5 + 5 + 5 + 5 = 35$ _____

7. $4 + 4 + 4 + 4 + 4 + 4 = 24$ _____

8. **MARKERS** You buy 5 packs of 8 markers each. How many markers do you buy in all? _____

9. **CARTWHEELS** You do 3 sets of 6 cartwheels each. Your friend does 2 sets of 9 cartwheels each. How many cartwheels do you and your friend do in all? Explain. _____

_____

Name _____

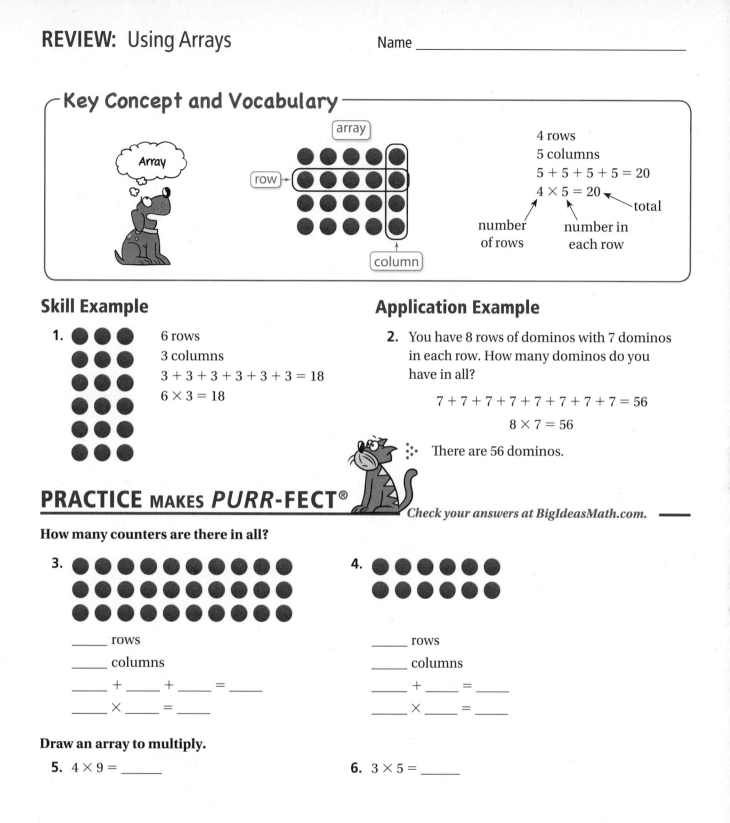

Key Concept and Vocabulary

Array

array

row →

column

4 rows
5 columns
$5 + 5 + 5 + 5 = 20$
$4 \times 5 = 20$ ← total

number of rows

number in each row

Skill Example

1. 6 rows
   3 columns
   $3 + 3 + 3 + 3 + 3 + 3 = 18$
   $6 \times 3 = 18$

Application Example

2. You have 8 rows of dominos with 7 dominos in each row. How many dominos do you have in all?

   $7 + 7 + 7 + 7 + 7 + 7 + 7 + 7 = 56$

   $8 \times 7 = 56$

   There are 56 dominos.

PRACTICE MAKES *PURR*-FECT®

Check your answers at BigIdeasMath.com.

How many counters are there in all?

3. _____ rows

   _____ columns

   _____ + _____ + _____ = _____

   _____ × _____ = _____

4. _____ rows

   _____ columns

   _____ + _____ = _____

   _____ × _____ = _____

Draw an array to multiply.

5. $4 \times 9 =$ _____

6. $3 \times 5 =$ _____

7. **GARDEN** A garden has 7 rows of 6 carrots each. How many carrots are there in all? _____

8. **HIP HOP DANCE** A hip hop dance team is arranged into 2 equal rows. There are 16 dancers in all. How many dancers are in each row? Explain. _____

_____

REVIEW: Multiplication Facts

Name _____

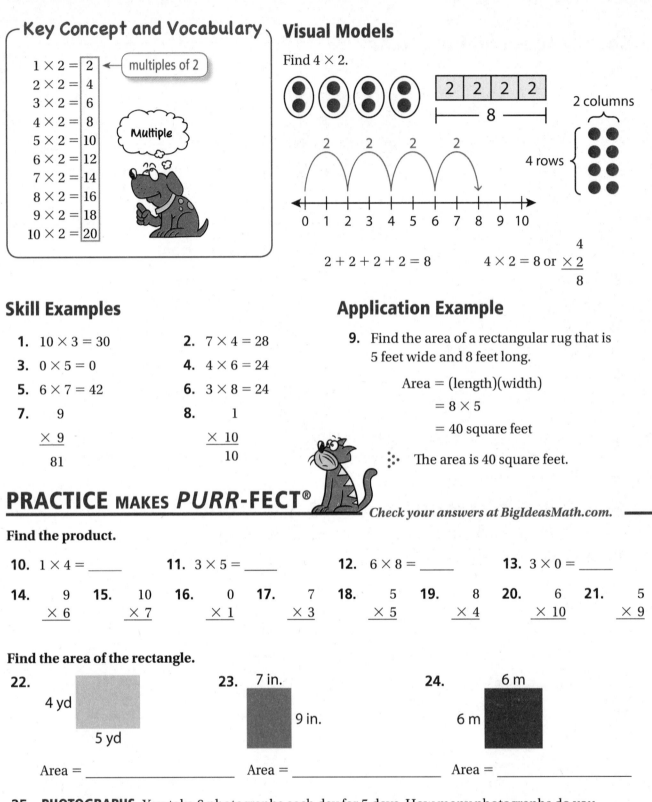

Key Concept and Vocabulary

$1 \times 2 = 2$ ← multiples of 2
$2 \times 2 = 4$
$3 \times 2 = 6$
$4 \times 2 = 8$
$5 \times 2 = 10$
$6 \times 2 = 12$
$7 \times 2 = 14$
$8 \times 2 = 16$
$9 \times 2 = 18$
$10 \times 2 = 20$

Multiple

Visual Models

Find 4×2.

| 2 | 2 | 2 | 2 |

8

2 columns

4 rows

$2 + 2 + 2 + 2 = 8$

$4 \times 2 = 8$ or $\begin{array}{r} 4 \\ \times 2 \\ \hline 8 \end{array}$

Skill Examples

1. $10 \times 3 = 30$
2. $7 \times 4 = 28$
3. $0 \times 5 = 0$
4. $4 \times 6 = 24$
5. $6 \times 7 = 42$
6. $3 \times 8 = 24$
7. $\begin{array}{r} 9 \\ \times 9 \\ \hline 81 \end{array}$
8. $\begin{array}{r} 1 \\ \times 10 \\ \hline 10 \end{array}$

Application Example

9. Find the area of a rectangular rug that is 5 feet wide and 8 feet long.

$Area = (length)(width)$
$= 8 \times 5$
$= 40$ square feet

∴ The area is 40 square feet.

PRACTICE MAKES PURR-FECT®

Check your answers at BigIdeasMath.com.

Find the product.

10. $1 \times 4 =$ _____
11. $3 \times 5 =$ _____
12. $6 \times 8 =$ _____
13. $3 \times 0 =$ _____

14. $\begin{array}{r} 9 \\ \times 6 \\ \hline \end{array}$
15. $\begin{array}{r} 10 \\ \times 7 \\ \hline \end{array}$
16. $\begin{array}{r} 0 \\ \times 1 \\ \hline \end{array}$
17. $\begin{array}{r} 7 \\ \times 3 \\ \hline \end{array}$
18. $\begin{array}{r} 5 \\ \times 5 \\ \hline \end{array}$
19. $\begin{array}{r} 8 \\ \times 4 \\ \hline \end{array}$
20. $\begin{array}{r} 6 \\ \times 10 \\ \hline \end{array}$
21. $\begin{array}{r} 5 \\ \times 9 \\ \hline \end{array}$

Find the area of the rectangle.

22. 4 yd, 5 yd

Area = _____

23. 7 in., 9 in.

Area = _____

24. 6 m, 6 m

Area = _____

25. **PHOTOGRAPHS** You take 6 photographs each day for 5 days. How many photographs do you take in all? _____

26. **BAND CONCERT** A music teacher needs to make 4 rows of 9 chairs each for a band concert. He has 35 chairs. Does he have enough chairs for the band concert? Explain. _____

_____

REVIEW: Equal Groups and Division

Name _____

Key Concept and Vocabulary

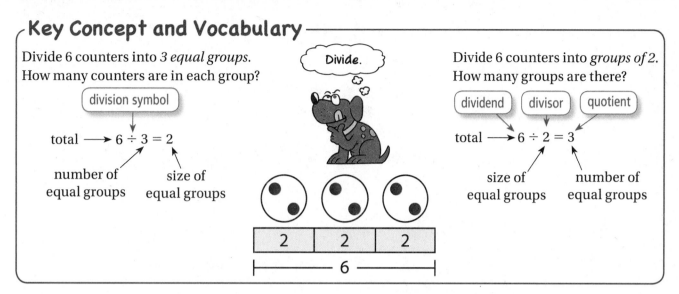

Divide 6 counters into *3 equal groups*. How many counters are in each group?

division symbol

total → 6 ÷ 3 = 2

number of equal groups

size of equal groups

Divide.

Divide 6 counters into *groups of 2*. How many groups are there?

dividend   divisor   quotient

total → 6 ÷ 2 = 3

size of equal groups

number of equal groups

2   2   2

6

Skill Example

1. Divide 20 counters into 5 equal groups. How many counters are in each group?

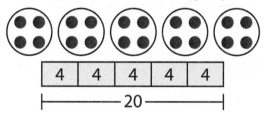

4   4   4   4   4

20

20 ÷ 5 = 4

Application Example

2. A football coach divides 42 players into groups of 7. How many groups are there?

42 ÷ 7 = 6

There are 6 groups.

PRACTICE MAKES *PURR*-FECT®

Check your answers at BigIdeasMath.com.

3. Divide 16 counters into 2 equal groups. How many counters are in each group?

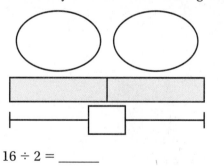

16 ÷ 2 = _____

4. Divide 24 counters into groups of 6. How many groups are there?

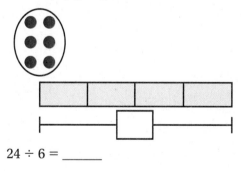

24 ÷ 6 = _____

5. **FLOWERS** You have 27 flowers. You put an equal number of flowers in each of 3 vases. How many flowers are in each vase? _____

6. **SURFBOARDS** A beach shop owner puts 80 stickers on surfboards. She puts 8 stickers on each surfboard. How many surfboards are there? _____

REVIEW: Division Facts

Name _____

Key Concept and Vocabulary

Find $8 \div 2$.

Think: 2 times what number is 8?

$2 \times 4 = 8$. So, $8 \div 2 = 4$.

Divide.

Visual Models

Find $8 \div 2$.

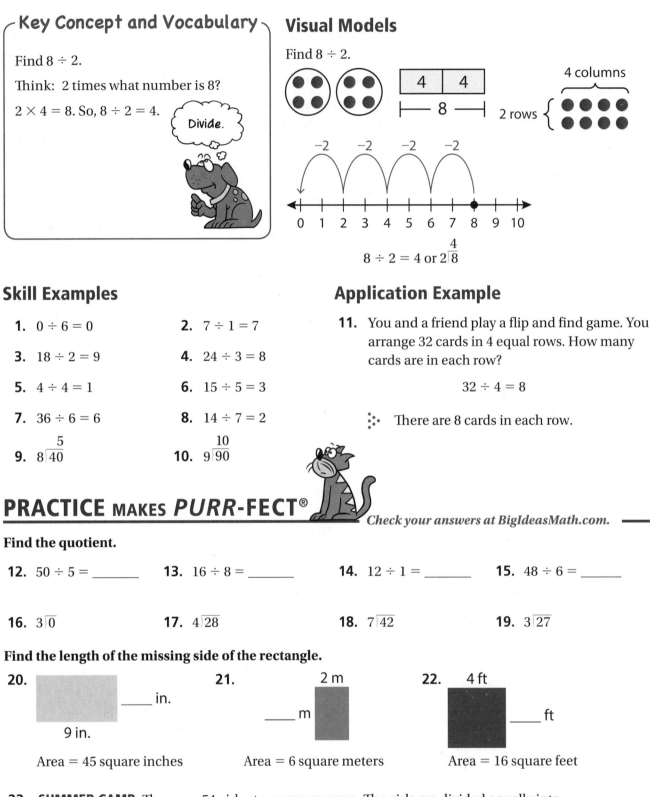

$$8 \div 2 = 4 \text{ or } 2\overline{)8}^{\,4}$$

Skill Examples

1. $0 \div 6 = 0$
2. $7 \div 1 = 7$
3. $18 \div 2 = 9$
4. $24 \div 3 = 8$
5. $4 \div 4 = 1$
6. $15 \div 5 = 3$
7. $36 \div 6 = 6$
8. $14 \div 7 = 2$
9. $8\overline{)40}^{\,5}$
10. $9\overline{)90}^{\,10}$

Application Example

11. You and a friend play a flip and find game. You arrange 32 cards in 4 equal rows. How many cards are in each row?

$$32 \div 4 = 8$$

⋮⋮ There are 8 cards in each row.

PRACTICE MAKES PURR-FECT®

Check your answers at BigIdeasMath.com.

Find the quotient.

12. $50 \div 5 = $ _____

13. $16 \div 8 = $ _____

14. $12 \div 1 = $ _____

15. $48 \div 6 = $ _____

16. $3\overline{)0}$

17. $4\overline{)28}$

18. $7\overline{)42}$

19. $3\overline{)27}$

Find the length of the missing side of the rectangle.

20. _____ in.

9 in.

Area = 45 square inches

21. 2 m

_____ m

Area = 6 square meters

22. 4 ft

_____ ft

Area = 16 square feet

23. **SUMMER CAMP** There are 54 girls at a summer camp. The girls are divided equally into 6 cabins. How many girls are in each cabin? _____

24. **RECYCLING** You recycle the same number of bottles each day for 7 days. You recycle 29 plastic bottles and 27 glass bottles altogether. How many bottles do you recycle each day? Explain. _____

REVIEW: Multiplying and Dividing by Powers of 10

Name _____

Key Concept and Vocabulary

$7 \times 1 = 7$

$7 = 10^1 = 7 \times 10 = 70.$

$7 \times 10^2 = 7 \times 100 = 700.$

Patterns

$7 \div 1 = 7$

$7 \div 10^1 = 7 \div 10 = 0.7$

$7 \div 10^2 = 7 \div 100 = 0.07$

Visual Models

	Hundreds	Tens	Ones	.	Tenths
$7 \times 1 = 7$			7	.	
$7 \times 10^1 = 70$		7	0	.	
$7 \times 10^2 = 700$	7	0	0	.	

	Tens	Ones	.	Tenths	Hundredths
$7 \div 1 = 7$		7	.		
$7 \div 10^1 = 0.7$		0	.	7	
$7 \div 10^2 = 0.07$		0	.	0	7

Skill Examples

1. $600 \times 100 = 60{,}000$

2. $21{,}398 \div 10 = 2{,}139.8$

3. $905 \times 10^3 = 905{,}000$

4. $467 \div 10^2 = 4.67$

5. $3 \times 10^4 = 30{,}000$

6. $82 \div 10^3 = 0.082$

Application Example

7. A store owner orders 100 identical laptops. He pays $49,999 in all. How much money does each laptop cost?

$\$49{,}999 \div 100 = \$499.99$

Each laptop costs $499.99.

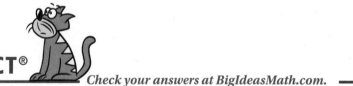

PRACTICE MAKES PURR-FECT®

Check your answers at BigIdeasMath.com.

Find the product or quotient.

8. $5 \times 1{,}000 =$ _____

9. $12 \times 10{,}000 =$ _____

10. $389 \times 10^1 =$ _____

11. $44 \times 10^2 =$ _____

12. $30 \div 100 =$ _____

13. $601 \div 10 =$ _____

14. $9{,}564 \div 10^2 =$ _____

15. $225 \div 10^3 =$ _____

16. $8{,}940 \div 10^2 =$ _____

17. $26 \times 10^3 =$ _____

18. $1 \div 10^3 =$ _____

19. $34 \times 10^4 =$ _____

Complete the equation.

20. $9 \times$ _____ $= 90{,}000$

21. $561 \div$ _____ $= 5.61$

22. _____ $\div 10^3 = 1.937$

23. **TOTEM POLE** A totem pole is 240 inches tall. The totem pole is made of 10 wooden animals of the same height. How many inches tall is each animal? _____

REVIEW: Multiplying Multi-Digit Numbers

Name _____

Key Concept and Vocabulary

```
     1
    13  ← factors
 ×  24
    52  ← partial products
 + 260
   312  ← product
```

Multiply.

Visual Model

```
200   10 × 20
 40   10 × 4
 60    3 × 20
+ 12   3 × 4
312
```

Skill Examples

1.
```
   5 2
   263
 ×  91
   263
 + 23,670
   23,933
```

∴ $263 \times 91 = 23{,}933$

2.
```
   2 3
  7,056
 ×   15
  35,280
 + 70,560
  105,840
```

∴ $7{,}056 \times 15 = 105{,}840$

Application Example

3. Find the area of the floor of a rectangular room that is 7 meters wide and 15 meters long.

$$\text{Area} = (\text{length})(\text{width})$$
$$= 7 \times 15$$
$$= 105 \text{ square meters}$$

∴ The area is 105 square meters.

PRACTICE MAKES PURR-FECT®

Check your answers at BigIdeasMath.com.

Find the product.

4. $51 \times 6 =$ _____

5. $240 \times 2 =$ _____

6. $14 \times 17 =$ _____

7. $19 \times 21 =$ _____

8. $100 \times 30 =$ _____

9. $206 \times 17 =$ _____

10. $3{,}792 \times 5 =$ _____

11. $2{,}054 \times 41 =$ _____

12. $23{,}652 \times 9 =$ _____

13. $3{,}196 \times 41 =$ _____

14. $5 \times 309 \times 2 =$ _____

Find the area of the rectangle.

15.

62 ft
85 ft

Area = _____

16. 89 m

107 m

Area = _____

17. 36 in.

36 in.

Area = _____

18. SCHOOL BUS Each school bus can carry a maximum of 50 passengers. What is the maximum number of passengers that 12 school buses can carry? _____

19. PAPER CUPS Each package contains 65 paper cups. You buy four packages. Do you have enough paper cups for 250 people to each have one? How do you know? _____

_____

REVIEW: Dividing Multi-Digit Numbers

Name _____

Key Concept and Vocabulary

$$\begin{array}{r} 5\ R2 \\ 4\overline{)22} \\ -20 \\ \hline 2 \end{array}$$

Divide.

remainder

Visual Model

$22 \div 4 = 5\ R2$

Skill Examples

1.
$$\begin{array}{r} 13 \\ 15\overline{)195} \\ 15 \\ \hline 45 \\ -45 \\ \hline 0 \end{array}$$

$195 \div 15 = 13$

2.
$$\begin{array}{r} 86\ R5 \\ 25\overline{)2{,}155} \\ -200\downarrow \\ \hline 155 \\ -150 \\ \hline 5 \end{array}$$

$2{,}155 \div 25 = 86\ R5$

Application Example

3. Six people together find a treasure worth $9,300. Each person receives an equal share. How much money does each person get?

$$\$9{,}300 \div 6 = \$1{,}550$$

Each person gets $1,550.

PRACTICE MAKES PURR-FECT®

Check your answers at BigIdeasMath.com.

Divide.

4. $56 \div 4 =$ _____

5. $132 \div 6 =$ _____

6. $44 \div 5 =$ _____

7. $845 \div 3 =$ _____

8. $6{,}321 \div 7 =$ _____

9. $2{,}894 \div 9 =$ _____

10. $414 \div 46 =$ _____

11. $3{,}082 \div 23 =$ _____

12. $8\overline{)216}$

13. $12\overline{)960}$

14. $41\overline{)567}$

15. $19\overline{)3{,}286}$

Find the length of the missing side of the rectangle.

16. _____ ft   86 ft   Area = 7,912 square feet

17. _____ m   52 m   Area = 676 square meters

18. _____ in.   42 in.   Area = 1,764 square inches

19. **PARTY PUNCH** A punch bowl contains 6 quarts of punch. There are 32 fluid ounces in a quart. How many 4-fluid ounce cups will the punch bowl serve? _____

20. **SHARING THE PROFIT** You and three friends start a small business. The total income is $1,820 and the total expenses are $360. You share the profit evenly. How much do each of you get? Explain. _____

_____

REVIEW: Interpreting Remainders

Name _____

Key Concept and Vocabulary

Tours of a museum can have no more than 8 guests. There are 30 guests in line to tour the museum. How many tours are needed?

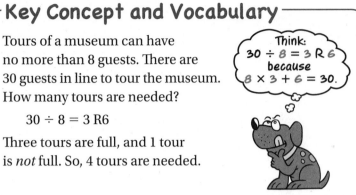

Think:
$30 \div 8 = 3\,R\,6$
because
$8 \times 3 + 6 = 30$.

$30 \div 8 = 3\,R6$

Three tours are full, and 1 tour is *not* full. So, 4 tours are needed.

Visual Model

Divide 30 into equal groups of 8.

There are 3 equal groups of 8, with 1 group of 6 left over. There are 4 groups in all.

Application Example

1. Seventy-nine players sign up for a basketball league. Teams can have no more than 10 players.

$$79 \div 10 = 7\,R9$$

- How many teams are full?
  - The quotient is the number of teams that have 10 players. So, 7 teams are full.

- How many teams are needed?
  - Seven teams are full and 1 team is *not* full. So, 8 teams are needed.

- How many players are on the last team?
  - The remainder is the number of players that are on the last team.

So, 9 players are on the last team.

PRACTICE MAKES *PURR*-FECT®

Check your answers at BigIdeasMath.com.

2. You can fit no more than 6 candles in a box. You have 47 candles. How many boxes do you need?

_____

3. Eighty-four students attend math team tryouts. Each team must have 5 students. How many students will *not* be on a team?

_____

4. A factory has 1,254 tires. Each new car needs 4 tires. How many new cars can be made?

_____

5. **READING** A book has 121 pages. You have already read 91 pages. To finish the book, you decide to read 7 pages each day. How many days will it take you to finish the book?

_____

6. **FIELD DAY** Three classes of 26 students each sign up for a field day. Teams can have no more than 9 students. How many teams are full? How many students are on the last team? Explain.

_____

_____

REVIEW: Factors of Whole Numbers

Name _____

Key Concept and Vocabulary

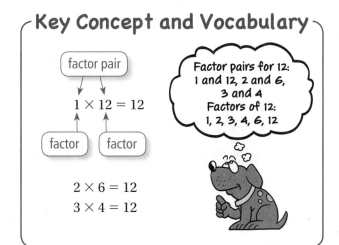

factor pair

$1 \times 12 = 12$

factor   factor

$2 \times 6 = 12$
$3 \times 4 = 12$

Factor pairs for 12:
1 and 12, 2 and 6,
3 and 4
Factors of 12:
1, 2, 3, 4, 6, 12

Visual Model

The side lengths of rectangles with an area of 12 square units represent the factor pairs for 12.

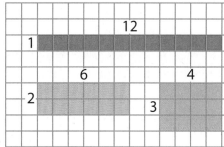

A 1×12 rectangle and a 12×1 rectangle both give the factor pair 1 and 12.

Skill Examples

1. Factors of 1: 1

2. Factors of 8: 1, 2, 4, 8

3. Factors of 7: 1, 7

4. Factors of 15: 1, 3, 5, 15

5. Factors of 29: 1, 29

Application Example

6. A car show director wants to organize 24 cars into a rectangular array. How many different arrays can he make?

   There are 4 factor pairs for 24.

   You can use each factor pair to make 2 arrays.

   $$4 \times 2 = 8$$

   ⁞∴ He can make 8 different arrays.

PRACTICE MAKES *PURR-FECT*®

Check your answers at BigIdeasMath.com.

7. Draw rectangles to find the factor pairs for 16.

Find the factor pairs for the number.

8. 6 _____

9. 11 _____

10. 30 _____

List the factors of the number.

11. 9 _____

12. 20 _____

13. 18 _____

14. **STEPPING STONE** You want to organize 10 pebbles into a rectangular array on a stepping stone. How many different arrays can you make? _____

15. **POSTERS** You have 40 posters to hang in a rectangular array on a wall. You do not have room for more than 8 posters in each row or column. What are the possible numbers of posters you can hang in each row? Explain. _____

REVIEW: Divisibility Tests

Key Concept and Vocabulary

A whole number is divisible by

2: if the number is even.

3: if the sum of the digits is divisible by 3.

5: if the ones digit is 0 or 5.

6: if the number is even and divisible by 3.

9: if the sum of the digits is divisible by 9.

10: if the ones digit is 0.

Skill Examples

1. 48 is divisible by 3 because
   $4 + 8 = 12$ is divisible by 3.

   ⋮· So, 3 is a factor of 48.

2. 243 is divisible by 9 because
   $2 + 4 + 3 = 9$ is divisible by 9.

   ⋮· So, 9 is a factor of 243.

Application Example

3. There are 127 chairs in the lunch room. Can you arrange the chairs into 5 equal rows?

   The ones digit of 127 is not 0 or 5, it is 7.

   ⋮· No, you cannot arrange the chairs into 5 equal rows.

PRACTICE MAKES *PURR*-FECT®

Check your answers at BigIdeasMath.com.

Use a divisibility test to answer the question.

4. Is 34 divisible by 2? _____

5. Is 79 divisible by 6? _____

6. Is 170 divisible by 10? _____

7. Is 5 a factor of 55? _____

8. Is 9 a factor of 81? _____

9. Is 3 a factor of 952? _____

Determine whether the length of the missing side of the rectangle is a whole number.

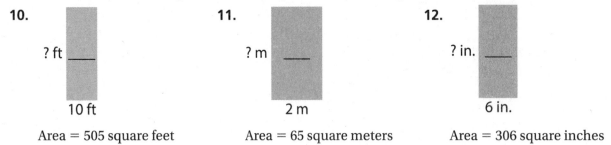

10.

? ft ____

10 ft

Area = 505 square feet

11.

? m ____

2 m

Area = 65 square meters

12.

? in. ____

6 in.

Area = 306 square inches

13. **CHARITY** A game show contestant wins $975. Can he divide his winnings equally among 9 different charities? Explain. _____

14. **SHARING TIME** A family of 3 people share a total of 270 cell phone minutes each month. Can each person use the same number of minutes each month? If so, how many?

_____

REVIEW: Prime and Composite Numbers

Name _____

Key Concept and Vocabulary

A **prime number** is a whole number greater than 1 with exactly two factors, 1 and itself.

A **composite number** is a whole number greater than 1 with more than two factors.

Divisibility tests can help you determine whether a number is prime or composite.

Skill Examples

1. 4 is even, so it is divisible by 2.
   4 has a factor in addition to 1 and itself.
   - So, 4 is *composite*.

2. 11 has exactly two factors, 1 and itself.
   - So, 11 is *prime*.

3. 75 is divisible by 3 because $7 + 5 = 12$ is divisible by 3.
   75 has factors in addition to 1 and itself.
   - So, 75 is *composite*.

Application Example

4. You collect 23 acorns. Can you separate the acorns into equal groups?

   23 has exactly two factors, 1 and itself.

   - You cannot separate the acorns into equal groups.

PRACTICE MAKES PURR-FECT®

Check your answers at BigIdeasMath.com.

Tell whether the number is *prime* or *composite*.

5. 2 _____
6. 5 _____
7. 51 _____

8. 7 _____
9. 36 _____
10. 48 _____

11. 60 _____
12. 85 _____
13. 13 _____

14. 19 _____
15. 54 _____
16. 29 _____

17. 49 _____
18. 37 _____
19. 72 _____

20. **MARCHING BAND** A marching band has 65 students. Can the band director arrange the students into a rectangular array with more than 1 row and more than 1 student in each row? Explain.

_____

_____

_____

21. **LISTING PRIME NUMBERS** List all the prime numbers that are less than 50.

_____

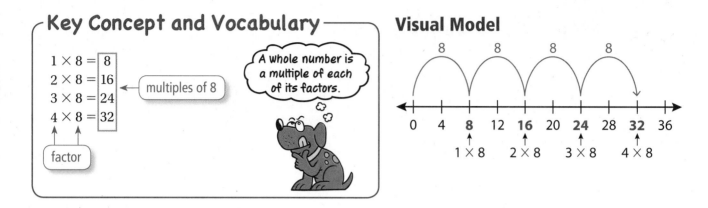

Key Concept and Vocabulary

$1 \times 8 = 8$
$2 \times 8 = 16$ ← multiples of 8
$3 \times 8 = 24$
$4 \times 8 = 32$

↑ ↑
factor

A whole number is a multiple of each of its factors.

Visual Model

8   8   8   8

0   4   **8**   12   **16**   20   **24**   28   **32**   36

1×8 2×8 3×8 4×8

Skill Examples

1. Is 12 a multiple of 4?

One Way: List multiples of 4: 4, 8, (12)

Another Way: Use division. 12 is divisible by 4, so 4 is a factor of 12.

⋮• So, 12 is a multiple of 4.

2. Is 5 a factor of 20?

One Way: List multiples of 5: 5, 10, 15, (20)

Another Way: Use division. 20 is divisible by 5.

⋮• So, 5 is a factor of 20.

Application Example

3. You need 60 tacos for a class fiesta. Tacos come in boxes of 3, boxes of 7, and boxes of 10. Which boxes could you buy so you have no leftover tacos?

60 is a multiple of 3 and 10.
60 is *not* a multiple of 7.

⋮• You could buy boxes of 3 tacos or boxes of 10 tacos.

PRACTICE MAKES *PURR*-FECT®

Check your answers at BigIdeasMath.com. ▬▬

4. Is 9 a multiple of 1? _____

5. Is 18 a multiple of 2? _____

6. Is 32 a multiple of 9? _____

7. Is 6 a factor of 46? _____

8. Is 18 a factor of 52? _____

9. Is 7 a factor of 63? _____

Tell whether 4 is a multiple or a factor of the number. Write *multiple, factor,* or *both*.

10. 24 _____

11. 4 _____

12. 2 _____

13. ROCKETS A teacher needs 35 model rockets for his students. Model rockets are sold in boxes of 3, boxes of 5, and boxes of 7. Which boxes could the teacher buy so he has no leftover rockets? _____

14. RUNNING A runner wants to run a total of 42 miles. She wants to run the same number of miles each day. Which numbers of miles can she run each day: 3, 4, 5, or 6? How many days will it take her to run the 42 miles? Explain. _____

_____

_____

REVIEW: Least Common Multiple

Name _____

Key Concept and Vocabulary

The **least common multiple (LCM)** of two or more positive numbers is the product of their factors, using each common prime factor only once.

Prime factorization:

$$30 = 2 \cdot 3 \cdot 5$$
$$42 = 2 \cdot 3 \cdot 7$$

The LCM of 30 and 42 is $2 \cdot 3 \cdot 5 \cdot 7 = 210$.

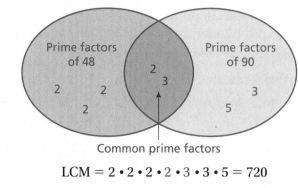

Visual Model

Prime factors of 48

Prime factors of 90

Common prime factors

$$LCM = 2 \cdot 2 \cdot 2 \cdot 2 \cdot 3 \cdot 3 \cdot 5 = 720$$

Skill Examples

1. $15 = 3 \cdot 5$
$30 = 2 \cdot 3 \cdot 5$
$LCM = 2 \cdot 3 \cdot 5 = 30$

2. $20 = 2 \cdot 2 \cdot 5$
$28 = 2 \cdot 2 \cdot 7$
$LCM = 2 \cdot 2 \cdot 5 \cdot 7 = 140$

3. $48 = 2 \cdot 2 \cdot 2 \cdot 2 \cdot 3$
$90 = 2 \cdot 3 \cdot 3 \cdot 5$
$LCM = 2 \cdot 2 \cdot 2 \cdot 2 \cdot 3 \cdot 3 \cdot 5 = 720$

4. $18 = 2 \cdot 3 \cdot 3$
$21 = 3 \cdot 7$
$LCM = 2 \cdot 3 \cdot 3 \cdot 7 = 126$

Application Example

5. Hot dogs come in packages of 10 and hot dog buns come in packages of 8. What is the least number of packages of each that you need to buy to have the same number of hot dogs and hot dog buns

$\left. \begin{array}{l} 10 = 2 \cdot 5 \\ 8 = 2 \cdot 2 \cdot 2 \end{array} \right\}$ $\begin{array}{l} LCM = 2 \cdot 2 \cdot 2 \cdot 5 \\ \qquad = 40 \end{array}$

$40 \div 10 = 4$ packages of hot dogs

$40 \div 8 = 5$ packages of hot dog buns

⋮• You must buy 4 packages of hot dogs and 5 packages of hot dog buns.

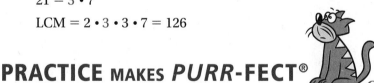

PRACTICE MAKES *PURR-FECT*®

Check your answers at BigIdeasMath.com.

Find the least common multiple.

6. 27 = _____   LCM = _____
54 = _____

7. 36 = _____   LCM = _____
45 = _____

8. 70 = _____   LCM = _____
98 = _____

9. 42 = _____   LCM = _____
105 = _____

10. 154 = _____   LCM = _____
231 = _____

11. 56 = _____   LCM = _____
68 = _____

12. BOXES Boxes that are 12 inches tall are being stacked next to boxes that are 18 inches tall. What is the shortest height at which the two stacks will be the same height? _____

Name _____

Key Concept and Vocabulary

The **greatest common factor (GCF)** of two or more positive numbers is the product of their common prime factors.

Prime factorization:

$$165 = 3 \cdot 5 \cdot 11$$
$$210 = 2 \cdot 3 \cdot 5 \cdot 7$$

The GCF of 165 and 210 is $3 \cdot 5 = 15$.

Visual Model

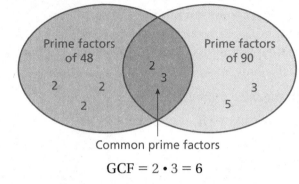

Common prime factors

$$GCF = 2 \cdot 3 = 6$$

Skill Examples

1. $15 = 3 \cdot 5$
   $30 = 2 \cdot 3 \cdot 5$
   $GCF = 3 \cdot 5 = 15$

2. $20 = 2 \cdot 2 \cdot 5$
   $28 = 2 \cdot 2 \cdot 7$
   $GCF = 2 \cdot 2 = 4$

3. $48 = 2 \cdot 2 \cdot 2 \cdot 2 \cdot 3$
   $90 = 2 \cdot 3 \cdot 3 \cdot 5$
   $GCF = 2 \cdot 3 = 6$

4. $18 = 2 \cdot 3 \cdot 3$
   $21 = 3 \cdot 7$
   $GCF = 3 = 3$

Application Example

5. You have 48 red flowers, 60 yellow flowers, and 84 white flowers. You want to make flower arrangements that have the same numbers of red, yellow, and white flowers. What is the greatest number of arrangements that you can make using all of the flowers?

$$48 = 2 \cdot 2 \cdot 2 \cdot 2 \cdot 3$$
$$60 = 2 \cdot 2 \cdot 3 \cdot 5$$
$$84 = 2 \cdot 2 \cdot 3 \cdot 7$$

$$GCF = 2 \cdot 2 \cdot 3 = 12$$

∴ You can make 12 arrangements.

PRACTICE MAKES *PURR-FECT®*

Check your answers at BigIdeasMath.com. ───

Find the greatest common factor.

6. $27 =$ _____ GCF = _____
   $54 =$ _____

7. $36 =$ _____ GCF = _____
   $45 =$ _____

8. $70 =$ _____ GCF = _____
   $98 =$ _____

9. $42 =$ _____ GCF = _____
   $105 =$ _____

10. $154 =$ _____ GCF = _____
    $231 =$ _____

11. $56 =$ _____ GCF = _____
    $68 =$ _____

12. **CLOTH** You have two pieces of cloth. One piece is 80 inches wide and the other is 96 inches wide. You want to cut both pieces of cloth into strips of equal width that are as wide as possible. How wide should you cut each strip?_____

REVIEW: Commutative and Associative Properties

Name _____

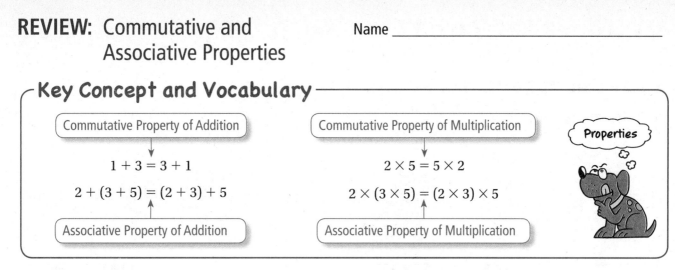

Key Concept and Vocabulary

Commutative Property of Addition

$$1 + 3 = 3 + 1$$

$$2 + (3 + 5) = (2 + 3) + 5$$

Associative Property of Addition

Commutative Property of Multiplication

$$2 \times 5 = 5 \times 2$$

$$2 \times (3 \times 5) = (2 \times 3) \times 5$$

Associative Property of Multiplication

Properties

Skill Examples

1. $3 + 6 = 6 + 3 = 9$

   Commutative Property of Addition

2. $15 + (5 + 3) = (15 + 5) + 3 = 23$

   Associative Property of Addition

3. $4 \times 6 = 6 \times 4 = 24$

   Commutative Property of Multiplication

4. $2 \times (3 \times 5) = (2 \times 3) \times 5 = 30$

   Associative Property of Multiplication

Application Example

5. On a field trip, there are 62 students, 4 teachers, and 8 volunteers. Use a property to find how many people are on the field trip in all.

$$62 + 4 + 8 = 62 + 8 + 4 \qquad \text{Commutative Property of Addition}$$
$$= 70 + 4$$
$$= 74$$

There are 74 people on the field trip.

PRACTICE MAKES PURR-FECT®

Check your answers at BigIdeasMath.com.

Identify the property. The find the sum or product.

6. $11 + 36 = 36 + 11$

   _____

7. $10 \times 4 = 4 \times 10$

   _____

8. $5 \times (4 \times 2) = (5 \times 4) \times 2$

   _____

9. $2 + (3 + 5) = (2 + 3) + 5$

   _____

10. $2 + 3 + 4 = 2 + 4 + 3$

    _____

11. $5 \times 2 \times 3 = 2 \times 5 \times 3$

    _____

Show how you can use properties to find the sum or product.

12. $15 + 13 + 35 + 27 =$ _____

    _____

    _____

13. $9 \times 5 \times 3 \times 2 =$ _____

    _____

    _____

14. **COMMUTATIVITY** Describe two real-life activities that are *not* commutative. In other words, you get different results if you switch the order in which the activities are performed.

_____

REVIEW: Distributive Property

Name _____

Key Concept and Vocabulary

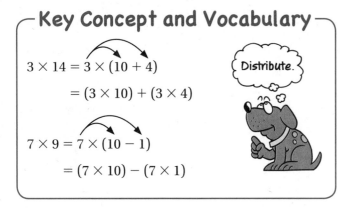

$3 \times 14 = 3 \times (10 + 4)$

$\qquad = (3 \times 10) + (3 \times 4)$

$7 \times 9 = 7 \times (10 - 1)$

$\qquad = (7 \times 10) - (7 \times 1)$

Distribute.

Visual Model

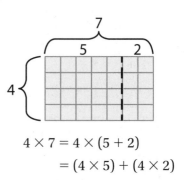

$4 \times 7 = 4 \times (5 + 2)$

$\qquad = (4 \times 5) + (4 \times 2)$

Skill Examples

1. $13 \times 6 = (10 + 3) \times 6$

$\qquad = (10 \times 6) + (3 \times 6)$

$\qquad = 60 + 18$

$\qquad = 78$

2. $5 \times 19 = 5 \times (20 - 1)$

$\qquad = (5 \times 20) - (5 \times 1)$

$\qquad = 100 - 5$

$\qquad = 95$

Application Example

3. A coach buys 6 blue hats and 6 red hats. Each hat costs $4. How much money does the coach spend?

$(6 + 6) \times 4 = (6 \times 4) + (6 \times 4)$

$\qquad = 24 + 24$

$\qquad = 48$

∴ The coach spends $48.

PRACTICE MAKES *PURR*-FECT®

Check your answers at BigIdeasMath.com.

Use the Distributive Property to rewrite the expression.

4. $3 \times (10 + 2)$

5. $(10 - 3) \times 7$

6. $6 \times (10 + 10 + 4)$

_____   _____   _____

Use the Distributive Property to find the product.

7. $8 \times 12 =$ _____

8. $11 \times 7 =$ _____

9. $3 \times 15 =$ _____

10. $18 \times 6 =$ _____

11. $4 \times 23 =$ _____

12. $9 \times 19 =$ _____

13. $5 \times 16 =$ _____

14. $29 \times 2 =$ _____

15. $8 \times 13 =$ _____

16. BAKING You have 3 packages of blueberry muffin mix and 2 packages of wild berry muffin mix. Each package makes 12 muffins. How many muffins can you bake?

_____

REVIEW: Properties of Zero and One

Name _____

Key Concept and Vocabulary

Addition Property of Zero

$$5 + 0 = 5$$

$$5 \times 0 = 0$$

Multiplication Property of Zero

$$5 \times 1 = 5$$

Multiplication Property of One

Properties

Skill Examples

1. $0 \times 9 = 0$

Multiplication Property of Zero

2. $1 \times 3 = 3$

Multiplication Property of One

3. $7 + 0 = 7$

Addition Property of Zero

Application Example

4. You buy 4 coloring books. Each coloring book costs $1. How much money do you spend?

$$4 \times 1 = 4$$

∴ You spend $4.

PRACTICE MAKES *PURR*-FECT®

Check your answers at BigIdeasMath.com.

Find the sum or product and identify the property.

5. $0 + 6 = $ _____

_____

6. $2 \times 1 = $ _____

_____

7. $10 \times 0 = $ _____

_____

8. $1 \times 25 = $ _____

_____

9. $17 + 0 = $ _____

_____

10. $0 \times 56 = $ _____

_____

Compare.

11. 3×0 ☐ 1×3

12. $8 + 0$ ☐ 8×0

13. 9×0 ☐ 0×10

14. 5×1 ☐ $0 + 5$

15. 7×0 ☐ $1 + 0$

16. 1×4 ☐ 4×1

17. PRIZES A group of 6 students wins a contest. The teacher gives 1 prize to each student in the group. How many prizes does the teacher give out? _____

18. SCHOOL PLAY Tickets to a school play cost $1 for adults and are free for students. How much does it cost for 3 adults and 5 students to attend the play? _____

REVIEW: Exponents and Powers

Name _____

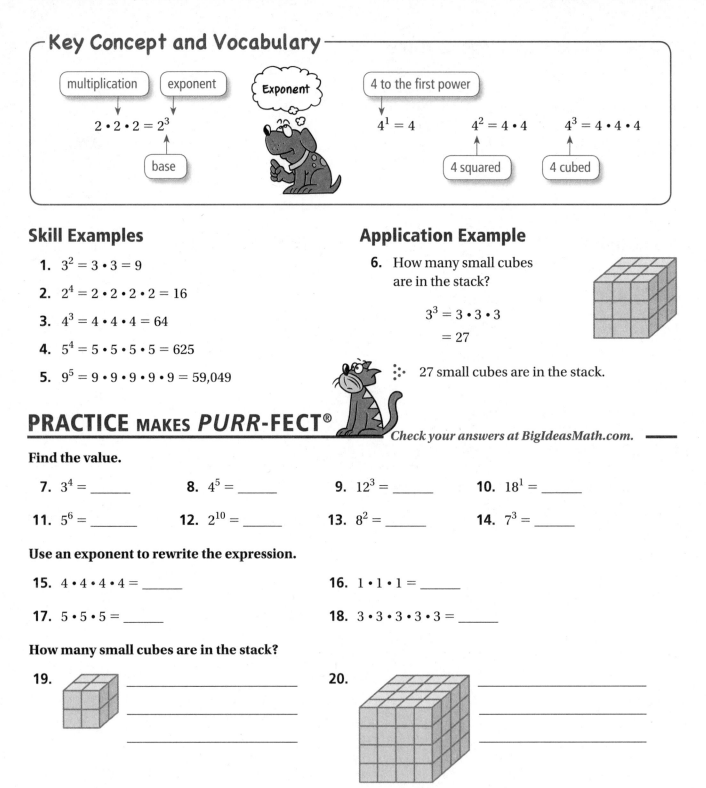

Key Concept and Vocabulary

multiplication   exponent

$$2 \cdot 2 \cdot 2 = 2^3$$

base

Exponent

4 to the first power

$$4^1 = 4 \qquad 4^2 = 4 \cdot 4 \qquad 4^3 = 4 \cdot 4 \cdot 4$$

4 squared   4 cubed

Skill Examples

1. $3^2 = 3 \cdot 3 = 9$

2. $2^4 = 2 \cdot 2 \cdot 2 \cdot 2 = 16$

3. $4^3 = 4 \cdot 4 \cdot 4 = 64$

4. $5^4 = 5 \cdot 5 \cdot 5 \cdot 5 = 625$

5. $9^5 = 9 \cdot 9 \cdot 9 \cdot 9 \cdot 9 = 59{,}049$

Application Example

6. How many small cubes are in the stack?

$$3^3 = 3 \cdot 3 \cdot 3$$
$$= 27$$

27 small cubes are in the stack.

PRACTICE MAKES *PURR-FECT*®

Check your answers at BigIdeasMath.com.

Find the value.

7. $3^4 =$ _____

8. $4^5 =$ _____

9. $12^3 =$ _____

10. $18^1 =$ _____

11. $5^6 =$ _____

12. $2^{10} =$ _____

13. $8^2 =$ _____

14. $7^3 =$ _____

Use an exponent to rewrite the expression.

15. $4 \cdot 4 \cdot 4 \cdot 4 =$ _____

16. $1 \cdot 1 \cdot 1 =$ _____

17. $5 \cdot 5 \cdot 5 =$ _____

18. $3 \cdot 3 \cdot 3 \cdot 3 \cdot 3 =$ _____

How many small cubes are in the stack?

19. _____
_____

20. _____
_____
_____

21. **FLYING SAUCERS** You saw 5 flying saucers. Each flying saucer had 5 aliens. Each alien had 5 eyes. How many alien eyes were there altogether? Explain your reasoning.

_____

REVIEW: Cube of a Number

Name _____

Key Concept and Vocabulary

multiplication   exponent   Cubes

$$2 \cdot 2 \cdot 2 = 2^3$$

base

Visual Model

$2^3 =$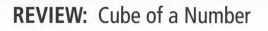

Skill Examples

1. $2^3 = 2 \cdot 2 \cdot 2 = 8$

2. $5^3 = 5 \cdot 5 \cdot 5 = 125$

3. $7^3 = 7 \cdot 7 \cdot 7 = 343$

4. $9^3 = 9 \cdot 9 \cdot 9 = 729$

5. $20^3 = 20 \cdot 20 \cdot 20 = 8000$

Application Example

6. How many small cubes are in the stack?

$$4^3 = 4 \cdot 4 \cdot 4$$
$$= 64$$

64 small cubes are in the stack.

PRACTICE MAKES *PURR*-FECT®

Check your answers at BigIdeasMath.com.

Find the value.

7. $6^3 = $ _____

8. $3^3 = $ _____

9. $8^3 = $ _____

10. $10^3 = $ _____

11. $12^3 = $ _____

12. $15^3 = $ _____

Use an exponent to rewrite the expression.

13. $16 \cdot 16 \cdot 16 = $ _____

14. $11 \cdot 11 \cdot 11 = $ _____

15. $25 \cdot 25 \cdot 25 = $ _____

Evaluate the expression when $x = 3$.

16. $x^3 + 1 = $ _____

17. $2x^3 = $ _____

18. $x^3 - 6x = $ _____

How many small cubes are in the stack?

19. _____

20. _____

21. **SHIPPING** How many boxes are stacked on the pallet? _____

REVIEW: Order of Operations

Name _____

Key Concept and Vocabulary

Order of Operations

1. Perform operations in parentheses.

2. Multiply and divide from left to right.

3. Add and subtract from left to right.

Simplify $5 + 3 \times 6 - 4$.

$$5 + 3 \times 6 - 4 = 5 + 18 - 4$$
$$= 23 - 4$$
$$= 19$$

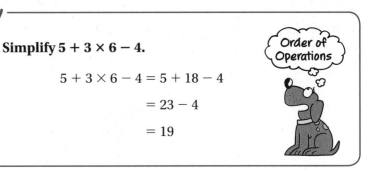

Skill Examples

1. $16 + 8 \div 4 = 16 + 2 = 18$

2. $3 \times 5 - 3 = 15 - 3 = 12$

3. $2 \times (3 - 1) = 2 \times 2 = 4$

4. $7 \times (16 \div 8) = 7 \times 2 = 14$

5. $4 + (8 - 6 \div 3) = 4 + (8 - 2) = 4 + 6 = 10$

Application Example

6. You buy 3 packs of trading cards. Each pack has 12 cards. You give 4 trading cards to your friend. Use the expression $3 \times 12 - 4$ to find how many trading cards you have now.

$$3 \times 12 - 4 = 36 - 4$$
$$= 32$$

∴ You have 32 trading cards.

PRACTICE MAKES *PURR-FECT*®

Check your answers at BigIdeasMath.com.

Evaluate the expression.

7. $8 - 6 \div 2 =$ _____

8. $3 \times 5 + 2 =$ _____

9. $20 \div 10 \times 2 =$ _____

10. $10 \times 4 - 3 =$ _____

11. $5 + 3 - 18 \div 3 =$ _____

12. $28 \div (25 - 18) =$ _____

13. $22 \div (14 - 3) =$ _____

14. $(18 - 4) \div 2 =$ _____

15. $15 - (4 + 15 \div 3) =$ _____

Insert parentheses to make the statement true.

16. $36 \div 6 - 2 = 9$

17. $24 \div 2 \times 4 + 5 = 8$

18. $9 + 4 \times 8 - 6 = 17$

19. **SOCKS** You order 12 pairs of socks that each cost $2. The order has a $7 shipping fee.

   a. Use the expression $12 \times 2 + 7$ to find how much you spend on the order. _____

   b. Each pair of socks is discounted $0.50. Use the expression $12 \times (2 - 0.5) + 7$ to find how much you spend on the order when the discount is applied. _____

REVIEW: Order of Operations with Exponents

Name _____

Key Concept and Vocabulary

Order of Operations

1. Perform operations in grouping symbols.
2. Evaluate numbers with exponents.
3. Multiply and divide from left to right.
4. Add and subtract from left to right.

Simplify $4^2 \div 2 + 3(9 - 5)$.

$$4^2 \div 2 + 3(9 - 5) = 4^2 \div 2 + 3 \cdot 4$$
$$= 16 \div 2 + 3 \cdot 4$$
$$= 8 + 12$$
$$= 20$$

Order of Operations

Skill Examples

1. $18 \div 2 - 4 = 9 - 4 = 5$

2. $2^2 \cdot (6 - 2) = 2^2 \cdot 4 = 4 \cdot 4 = 16$

3. $24 \div 2^3 - 1 = 24 \div 8 - 1 = 3 - 1 = 2$

4. $20 \div 10 + 21 \cdot 5 = 2 + 105 = 107$

5. $(2 + 3)^2 - 5 = 5^2 - 5 = 25 - 5 = 20$

Application Example

6. At a museum, 4 adults pay $15 each and 6 children pay $8 each. What is the total cost of the tickets?

$$4 \cdot 15 + 6 \cdot 8 = 60 + 48$$
$$= 108$$

The total cost is $108.

PRACTICE MAKES PURR-FECT®

Check your answers at BigIdeasMath.com.

Evaluate the expression.

7. $3^2 + 5(4 - 2) =$ _____

8. $3 + 4 \div 2 =$ _____

9. $10 \div 5 \cdot 3 =$ _____

10. $4(3^3 - 8) \div 2 =$ _____

11. $3 + 6^2 \div 2 =$ _____

12. $12 + 7 \cdot 3 - 24 =$ _____

Insert parentheses to make the statement true.

13. $5^2 - 15 \div 5 = 2$

14. $12 \cdot 2^3 + 4 = 144$

15. $91 - 21 \div 7 = 10$

Write an expression for the total area of the two rectangles. Evaluate your expression.

16.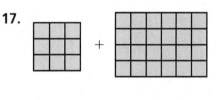

_____

17.

_____

18. **ADMISSION** At a baseball game, 6 adults pay $20 each and 4 children pay $10 each. What is the total cost of the tickets? _____

19. **INSERTING PARENTHESES** Insert parentheses in the expression $4 + 2^3 - 5 \cdot 2$ in two ways: (a) so that the value is 10 and (b) so that the value is 14.

(a) _____

(b) _____

REVIEW: Product of Powers Property

Name _____

Key Concept and Vocabulary

Product of Powers Property

To multiply powers with the same base, add their exponents.

Numbers: $2^3 \cdot 2^4 = 2^{3+4} = 2^7$

Algebra: $a^m \cdot a^n = a^{m+n}$

> Property

Visual Model

$2^3 \cdot 2^4 = (2 \cdot 2 \cdot 2) \cdot (2 \cdot 2 \cdot 2 \cdot 2)$

$\qquad = 2^7$

$(-4)^2 \cdot (-4)^3 = [(-4) \cdot (-4)][(-4) \cdot (-4) \cdot (-4)]$

$\qquad = (-4)^5$

Skill Examples

1. $5^2 \cdot 5^5 = 5^{2+5} = 5^7$

2. $(-3)^8 \cdot (-3)^2 = (-3)^{8+2} = (-3)^{10}$

3. $\left(7^2\right)^3 = 7^2 \cdot 7^2 \cdot 7^2 = 7^{2+2+2} = 7^6$

4. $\left(y^3\right)^4 = y^3 \cdot y^3 \cdot y^3 \cdot y^3 = y^{3+3+3+3} = y^{12}$

5. $(3x)^3 = 3x \cdot 3x \cdot 3x$

   $\qquad = (3 \cdot 3 \cdot 3) \cdot (x \cdot x \cdot x)$

   $\qquad = 3^3 \cdot x^3$

   $\qquad = 27x^3$

Application Example

6. A gigabyte of computer storage space is 2^{30} bytes. A computer has a total storage space of 128 gigabytes. How many bytes of total storage space does the computer have? Write your answer as a power.

   Notice that 128 can be written as a power, 2^7.

   $$\begin{array}{c} \text{Total number} \\ \text{of bytes} \end{array} = \begin{array}{c} \text{Number of bytes} \\ \text{in a gigabyte} \end{array} \cdot \begin{array}{c} \text{Number} \\ \text{of gigabytes} \end{array}$$

   $\qquad = 2^{30} \cdot 2^7$

   $\qquad = 2^{30+7}$

   $\qquad = 2^{37}$

   ⁞∴ The computer has 2^{37} bytes of total storage space.

PRACTICE MAKES *PURR-FECT*®

Check your answers at BigIdeasMath.com.

Simplify the expression. Write your answer as a power.

7. $8^3 \cdot 8^6 =$ _____

8. $3^4 \cdot 3^2 =$ _____

9. $6^7 \cdot 6^5 =$ _____

10. $(-5)^3 \cdot (-5)^7 =$ _____

11. $(-10)^6 \cdot (-10)^2 =$ _____

12. $(-2)^4 \cdot (-2)^5 =$ _____

13. $\left(9^4\right)^3 =$ _____

14. $\left(4^5\right)^3 =$ _____

15. $\left(12^3\right)^2 =$ _____

16. $\left(z^3\right)^3 =$ _____

17. $\left(n^5\right)^2 =$ _____

18. $\left(w^2\right)^4 =$ _____

Simplify the expression.

19. $(9y)^2 =$ _____

20. $(3b)^4 =$ _____

21. $(2a)^5 =$ _____

22. **ARTIFACT** A display case for the artifact is in the shape of a cube. Each side of the display case is four times the side length of the artifact. Write and simplify an expression for the volume of the case. _____

s in.

s in.

s in.

REVIEW: Quotient of Powers Property

Name _____

Key Concept and Vocabulary

Quotient of Powers Property

To divide powers with the same base, subtract their exponents.

Numbers: $\dfrac{3^6}{3^4} = 3^{6-4} = 3^2$

Algebra: $\dfrac{a^m}{a^n} = a^{m-n}, a \neq 0$

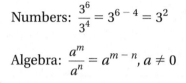

Visual Model

$$\frac{3^6}{3^4} = \frac{\overset{1}{\cancel{3}} \cdot \overset{1}{\cancel{3}} \cdot \overset{1}{\cancel{3}} \cdot \overset{1}{\cancel{3}} \cdot 3 \cdot 3}{\underset{1}{\cancel{3}} \cdot \underset{1}{\cancel{3}} \cdot \underset{1}{\cancel{3}} \cdot \underset{1}{\cancel{3}}} = 3 \cdot 3 = 3^2$$

$$\frac{(-4)^4}{(-4)^2} = \frac{(\overset{1}{\cancel{-4}}) \cdot (\overset{1}{\cancel{-4}}) \cdot (-4) \cdot (-4)}{(\underset{1}{\cancel{-4}}) \cdot (\underset{1}{\cancel{-4}})}$$

$$= (-4) \cdot (-4)$$

$$= (-4)^2$$

Skill Examples

1. $\dfrac{7^5}{7^2} = 7^{5-2} = 7^3$

2. $\dfrac{(-5)^9}{(-5)^4} = (-5)^{9-4} = (-5)^5$

3. $\dfrac{x^8}{x^6} = x^{8-6} = x^2$

Application Example

4. The population of a city is about $4 \cdot 5^6$. The land area is about 5^4 square miles. Find the average number of people per square mile.

$$\text{People per square mile} = \frac{4 \cdot 5^6}{5^4}$$

$$= 4 \cdot \frac{5^6}{5^4}$$

$$= 4 \cdot 5^2$$

$$= 100$$

There are about 100 people per square mile.

PRACTICE MAKES PURR-FECT®

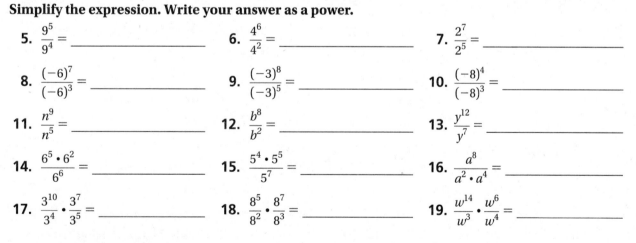

Check your answers at BigIdeasMath.com.

Simplify the expression. Write your answer as a power.

5. $\dfrac{9^5}{9^4} =$ _____

6. $\dfrac{4^6}{4^2} =$ _____

7. $\dfrac{2^7}{2^5} =$ _____

8. $\dfrac{(-6)^7}{(-6)^3} =$ _____

9. $\dfrac{(-3)^8}{(-3)^5} =$ _____

10. $\dfrac{(-8)^4}{(-8)^3} =$ _____

11. $\dfrac{n^9}{n^5} =$ _____

12. $\dfrac{b^8}{b^2} =$ _____

13. $\dfrac{y^{12}}{y^7} =$ _____

14. $\dfrac{6^5 \cdot 6^2}{6^6} =$ _____

15. $\dfrac{5^4 \cdot 5^5}{5^7} =$ _____

16. $\dfrac{a^8}{a^2 \cdot a^4} =$ _____

17. $\dfrac{3^{10}}{3^4} \cdot \dfrac{3^7}{3^5} =$ _____

18. $\dfrac{8^5}{8^2} \cdot \dfrac{8^7}{8^3} =$ _____

19. $\dfrac{w^{14}}{w^3} \cdot \dfrac{w^6}{w^4} =$ _____

20. **SOUND INTENSITY** The sound intensity of busy street traffic is 10^7 times greater than the quietest noise a person can hear. The sound intensity of the front rows at a rock concert is 10^{11} times greater than the quietest noise a person can hear. How many times more intense is the sound in the front rows of a rock concert than the sound of busy street traffic? _____

REVIEW: Zero and Negative Exponents

Name _____

Key Concept and Vocabulary

Zero Exponents

Any nonzero number to the zero power is equal to 1. Zero to the zero power, 0^0, is undefined.

Numbers: $6^0 = 1$

Algebra: $a^0 = 1$, where $a \neq 0$

Negative Exponents

For any integer n and any number a not equal to 0, a^{-n} is equal to 1 divided by a^n.

Numbers: $4^{-2} = \dfrac{1}{4^2}$

Algebra: $a^{-n} = \dfrac{1}{a^n}$, where $a \neq 0$

Skill Examples

1. $5^{-3} = \dfrac{1}{5^3} = \dfrac{1}{125}$

2. $3^{-6} \cdot 3^6 = 3^{-6+6} = 3^0 = 1$

3. $\dfrac{4^2}{4^5} = 4^{2-5} = 4^{-3} = \dfrac{1}{4^3} = \dfrac{1}{64}$

4. $\dfrac{7b^{-4}}{b^3} = 7b^{-4-3} = 7b^{-7} = \dfrac{7}{b^7}$

Application Example

5. A faucet leaks water at a rate of 5^{-4} liter per second. How many liters of water leak from the faucet in 1 hour?

   There are 3600 seconds in 1 hour. Multiply the time by the rate.

   $$3600 \times 5^{-4} = 3600 \cdot \dfrac{1}{5^4}$$
   $$= 3600 \cdot \dfrac{1}{625}$$
   $$= 5\dfrac{19}{25} = 5.76$$

   So, 5.76 liters of water leak from the faucet in 1 hour.

PRACTICE MAKES *PURR-FECT*®

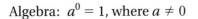

Check your answers at BigIdeasMath.com.

Evaluate the expression.

6. $4^{-4} =$ _____

7. $8^{-2} =$ _____

8. $(-5)^{-6} =$ _____

9. $9^{-4} \cdot 9^4 =$ _____

10. $\dfrac{2^3}{2^8} =$ _____

11. $\dfrac{5^3}{5^5} =$ _____

12. $\dfrac{(-4)^4}{(-4)^6} =$ _____

13. $\dfrac{1}{3^{-3}} \cdot \dfrac{1}{3^7} =$ _____

14. $\dfrac{4^5 \cdot 4^{-2}}{4^4} =$ _____

Simplify. Write the expression using only positive exponents.

15. $\dfrac{3x^4}{x^9} =$ _____

16. $\dfrac{a^{-5}}{14a^8} =$ _____

17. $\dfrac{3w^{-4}}{w^{-2}} =$ _____

METRIC UNITS In Exercises 18–21, use the table.

18. How many millimeters are in a centimeter? _____

19. How many decimeters are in a micrometer? _____

20. How many nanometers are in a centimeter? _____

21. How many micrometers are in a millimeter? _____

Unit of Length	Length
decimeter	10^{-1} m
centimeter	10^{-2} m
millimeter	10^{-3} m
micrometer	10^{-6} m
nanometer	10^{-9} m

REVIEW: Scientific Notation

Name _____

Key Concept and Vocabulary

A number is written in **scientific notation** when it is represented as the product of a factor and a power of 10. The factor must be at least 1 and less than 10.

> The factor is at least 1 and less than 10.

> The power of 10 has an integer exponent.

$$6.3 \times 10^5$$

> Scientific notation

Writing Numbers in Standard Form

When writing a number from scientific notation to standard form, the absolute value of the exponent tells you how many places to move the decimal point.

Negative exponent

Move the decimal point to the left.

$$6.1 \times 10^{-3} = 0.0061$$
3

Positive exponent

Move the decimal point to the right.

$$2.75 \times 10^5 = 275,000$$
5

Writing Numbers in Scientific Notation

Step 1: Move the decimal point to the right of the first nonzero digit.

Step 2: Count the number of places you moved the decimal point. This determines the exponent of the power of 10.

Number greater than or equal to 10

Use a positive exponent when you move the decimal point to the left.

$$3400 = 3.4 \times 10^3$$

Number between 0 and 1

Use a negative exponent when you move the decimal point to the right.

$$0.00018 = 1.8 \times 10^{-4}$$

Skill Examples

1. $1.66 \times 10^{-5} = 0.0000166$
5

2. $3.1 \times 10^6 = 3,100,000$
6

3. $0.033 = 3.3 \times 10^{-2}$
2

4. $2400 = 2.4 \times 10^3$
3

PRACTICE MAKES *PURR*-FECT®

Check your answers at BigIdeasMath.com.

Write the number in standard form.

5. $9.6 \times 10^7 =$ _____

6. $2 \times 10^{-6} =$ _____

7. $7.875 \times 10^4 =$ _____

8. $4.53 \times 10^{-4} =$ _____

9. $8.9 \times 10^{-7} =$ _____

10. $5.16 \times 10^8 =$ _____

Write the number in scientific notation.

11. $80,000,000 =$ _____

12. $0.00815 =$ _____

13. $8,135,000,000 =$ _____

14. $0.000051 =$ _____

15. $0.00000009 =$ _____

16. $1,784,000 =$ _____

REVIEW: Comparing, Ordering, and Graphing Integers

Name _____

Key Concept and Vocabulary

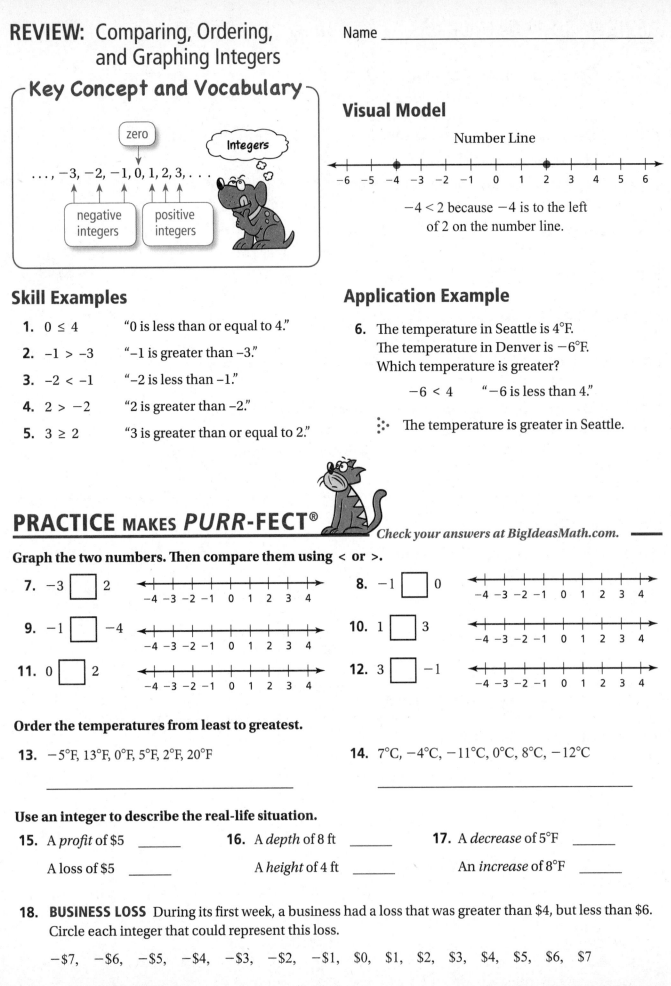

zero

Integers

$\ldots, -3, -2, -1, 0, 1, 2, 3, \ldots$

negative integers

positive integers

Visual Model

Number Line

$-4 < 2$ because -4 is to the left of 2 on the number line.

Skill Examples

1. $0 \leq 4$ "0 is less than or equal to 4."

2. $-1 > -3$ "−1 is greater than −3."

3. $-2 < -1$ "−2 is less than −1."

4. $2 > -2$ "2 is greater than −2."

5. $3 \geq 2$ "3 is greater than or equal to 2."

Application Example

6. The temperature in Seattle is 4°F. The temperature in Denver is −6°F. Which temperature is greater?

    $-6 < 4$ "−6 is less than 4."

    The temperature is greater in Seattle.

PRACTICE MAKES *PURR-FECT*®

Check your answers at BigIdeasMath.com.

Graph the two numbers. Then compare them using < or >.

7. -3 ☐ 2

8. -1 ☐ 0

9. -1 ☐ -4

10. 1 ☐ 3

11. 0 ☐ 2

12. 3 ☐ -1

Order the temperatures from least to greatest.

13. $-5°F, 13°F, 0°F, 5°F, 2°F, 20°F$

14. $7°C, -4°C, -11°C, 0°C, 8°C, -12°C$

_____

_____

Use an integer to describe the real-life situation.

15. A *profit* of $5 _____

     A loss of $5 _____

16. A *depth* of 8 ft _____

     A *height* of 4 ft _____

17. A *decrease* of 5°F _____

     An *increase* of 8°F _____

18. **BUSINESS LOSS** During its first week, a business had a loss that was greater than $4, but less than $6. Circle each integer that could represent this loss.

    $-$7, $-$6, $-$5, $-$4, $-$3, $-$2, $-$1, $0, $1, $2, $3, $4, $5, $6, $7

REVIEW: Absolute Value

Name _____

Key Concept and Vocabulary

The **absolute value** of a number is the distance between the number and 0 on a number line. The absolute value of a number is written as $|a|$.

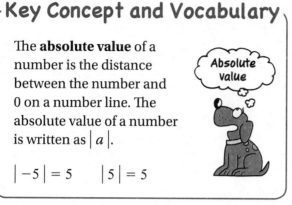

$|-5| = 5$ $|5| = 5$

Visual Model

$|-2| = 2$ $|2| = 2$

Skill Examples

1. $|12| = 12$
2. $|-8| = 8$
3. $|-22| = 22$
4. $|0| = 0$
5. $|-4.2| = 4.2$

Application Example

6. The table shows the elevations of two people at the ocean. Which person is farther from sea level?

   Person A: $|-4| = 4$

   Person B: $|3| = 3$

Person	Elevation (feet)
A	−4
B	3

∴ Because 4 is greater than 3, Person A is farther from sea level.

PRACTICE MAKES PURR-FECT®

Check your answers at BigIdeasMath.com.

Find the absolute value.

7. $|18| =$ _____

8. $|-1| =$ _____

9. $|-9| =$ _____

10. $|1.8| =$ _____

11. $|-5.5| =$ _____

12. $\left|-\dfrac{3}{4}\right| =$ _____

13. $\left|1\dfrac{2}{3}\right| =$ _____

14. $\left|-\dfrac{8}{5}\right| =$ _____

Complete the statement using <, >, or =.

15. $|-13|$ ☐ $|13|$

16. $|-5|$ ☐ 8

17. $|-12.1|$ ☐ $|-10.9|$

TEMPERATURE CHANGE The table shows the change in temperature each hour for 4 hours.

18. In which hour did the temperature increase the most? _____

19. In which hour did the temperature decrease the most? _____

20. In which hour did the temperature change the most? _____

21. In which hour did the temperature change the least? _____

Hour	Change in Temperature (°F)
1	−5
2	−2
3	6
4	4

REVIEW: Adding and Subtracting Integers

Name _____

Key Concept and Vocabulary

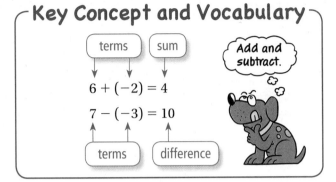

terms   sum

$$6 + (-2) = 4$$

$$7 - (-3) = 10$$

terms   difference

Add and subtract.

Visual Model

Positive numbers involve movement to the right. Negative numbers involve movement to the left.

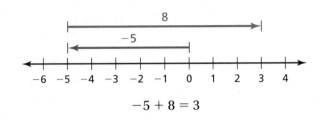

$$-5 + 8 = 3$$

Skill Examples

1. $5 + (-3) = 2$

2. $5 - (-2) = 5 + 2 = 7$

3. $-2 + 4 = 2$

4. $-3 - (-2) = -3 + 2 = -1$

5. $8 - (-3) = 8 + 3 = 11$

To subtract, add the opposite.

Application Example

6. The temperature is 8°F in the morning and drops to −5°F in the evening. What is the difference between these temperatures?

$$8 - (-5) = 8 + 5$$

$$= 13$$

∴ The difference is 13 degrees.

PRACTICE MAKES *PURR-FECT*®

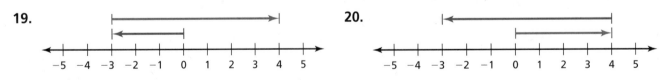

Check your answers at BigIdeasMath.com.

Find the sum or difference.

7. $-2 + 3 =$ _____

8. $-4 - 5 =$ _____

9. $8 - 2 =$ _____

10. $8 - (-2) =$ _____

11. $-4 - (-1) =$ _____

12. $-5 + (-5) =$ _____

13. $4 - (-8) =$ _____

14. $4 - 8 =$ _____

15. $-4 + (-6) =$ _____

16. $-4 - (-6) =$ _____

17. $10 - 13 =$ _____

18. $13 - (-10) =$ _____

Write the addition or subtraction shown by the number line.

19.

20.

21. **TEMPERATURE** The temperature is 16°F in the morning and drops to −15°F in the evening. What is the difference between these temperatures? _____

22. **SUBMARINE** A submarine is 450 feet below sea level. It descends 300 feet. What is its new position? Show your work.

_____

REVIEW: Multiplying and Dividing Integers

Name _____

Key Concept and Vocabulary

factors   product

$8 \cdot (-5) = -40$

$-12 \div (-3) = 4$

dividend   divisor   quotient

Visual Model

$$4 \cdot (-2) = (-2) + (-2) + (-2) + (-2)$$

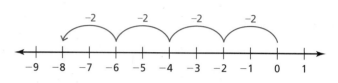

Skill Examples

1. $-3 \cdot (-4) = 12$ ← same sign, product and quotient positive
2. $-36 \div (-6) = 6$ ←
3. $-7 \cdot 0 = 0$
4. $-10 \div 5 = -2$ ← different signs, product and quotient negative
5. $-5 \cdot 6 = -30$ ←

Application Example

6. You pay six friends \$5 each from your bank account. Use integer multiplication to represent the change in the amount of money in your account.

$$6 \cdot (-5) = -30$$

∴ The amount of money in your bank account decreases \$30.

PRACTICE MAKES PURR-FECT®

Check your answers at BigIdeasMath.com.

Find the product or quotient.

7. $-3 \times (-5) =$ _____

8. $7(-3) =$ _____

9. $0 \cdot (-5) =$ _____

10. $(-5)(-7) =$ _____

11. $-8 \cdot 2 =$ _____

12. $(-5)^2 =$ _____

13. $(-3)^3 =$ _____

14. $4(-2)(-3) =$ _____

15. $-16 \div 4 =$ _____

16. $-20 \div (-5) =$ _____

17. $\dfrac{-9}{3} =$ _____

18. $\dfrac{-20}{-10} =$ _____

Complete the multiplication or division equation.

19. $-15 \div$ _____ $= -3$

20. $45 \div$ _____ $= -5$

21. _____ $\div (-20) = 5$

22. $8 \cdot$ _____ $= -64$

23. _____ $\cdot (-9) = 27$

24. $-12 \cdot$ _____ $= -96$

25. **BANK ACCOUNT** You pay eight friends \$10 each from your bank account. Use integer multiplication to represent the change in the amount of money in your account.

_____

26. **TEMPERATURE** The low temperatures for a week in Edmonton, Alberta are $-15°C$, $-12°C$, $-10°C$, $-12°C$, $-18°C$, $-20°C$, and $-25°C$. What is the mean low temperature for the week? Show your work.

_____

_____

REVIEW: The Coordinate Plane: First Quadrant

Name _____

Key Concept and Vocabulary

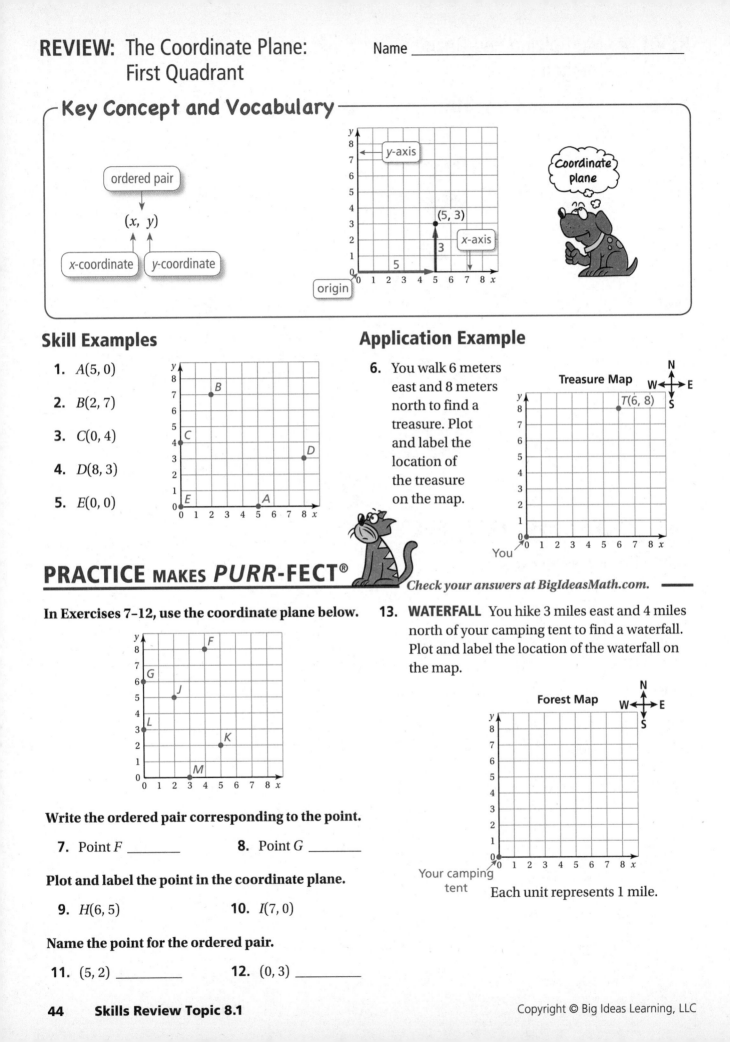

Skill Examples

1. $A(5, 0)$

2. $B(2, 7)$

3. $C(0, 4)$

4. $D(8, 3)$

5. $E(0, 0)$

Application Example

6. You walk 6 meters east and 8 meters north to find a treasure. Plot and label the location of the treasure on the map.

Treasure Map $T(6, 8)$

You

PRACTICE MAKES *PURR-FECT*®

Check your answers at BigIdeasMath.com. ━━

In Exercises 7–12, use the coordinate plane below.

Write the ordered pair corresponding to the point.

7. Point F _____

8. Point G _____

Plot and label the point in the coordinate plane.

9. $H(6, 5)$

10. $I(7, 0)$

Name the point for the ordered pair.

11. $(5, 2)$ _____

12. $(0, 3)$ _____

13. **WATERFALL** You hike 3 miles east and 4 miles north of your camping tent to find a waterfall. Plot and label the location of the waterfall on the map.

Forest Map

Your camping tent

Each unit represents 1 mile.

REVIEW: The Coordinate Plane

Name _____

Key Concept and Vocabulary

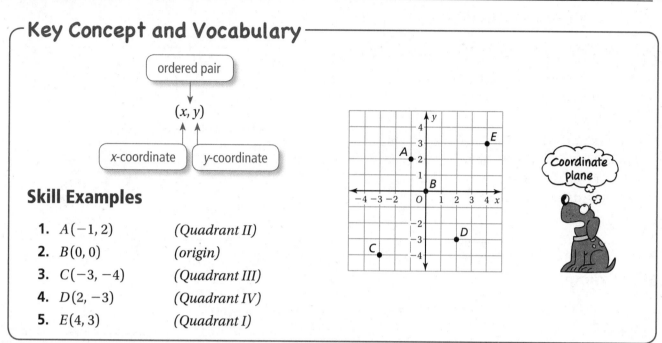

ordered pair

(x, y)

x-coordinate   y-coordinate

Skill Examples

1. $A(-1, 2)$ (Quadrant II)
2. $B(0, 0)$ (origin)
3. $C(-3, -4)$ (Quadrant III)
4. $D(2, -3)$ (Quadrant IV)
5. $E(4, 3)$ (Quadrant I)

PRACTICE MAKES PURR-FECT®

Check your answers at BigIdeasMath.com. —

Write the ordered pair corresponding to the point.

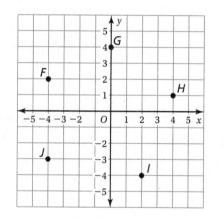

Plot the ordered pair in the coordinate plane. Name the quadrant for the point.

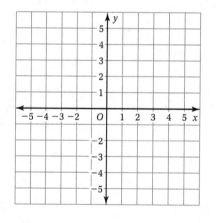

6. F _____

7. G _____

8. H _____

9. I _____

10. J _____

11. $K(-3, 5)$ _____

12. $L(-3, 0)$ _____

13. $M(2, 5)$ _____

14. $N(4, -2)$ _____

15. $P(-2, -4)$ _____

REVIEW: Finding Distance in a Coordinate Plane

Name _____

Key Concept and Vocabulary

Points A and B lie on the same horizontal line.
There are 5 units between points A and B.
So, the distance between points A and B is 5.

Points C and D lie on the same vertical line.
Points C and D have the same x-coordinates.
Subtract the y-coordinates. $3 - 1 = 2$.
So, the distance between points C and D is 2.

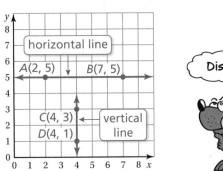

Skill Examples

Find the distance between the points in the coordinate plane.

1. E and F

   7

2. G and H

   3

Application Example

3. A construction crew places caution tape around a rectangular area of a road. How many yards of tape does the crew use?

$$P = (2 + \ell) + (2 \times w)$$
$$= (2 \times 8) + (2 \times 6)$$
$$= 16 + 12$$
$$= 28 \text{ yards}$$

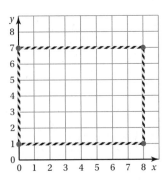

Each unit represents 1 yard.

PRACTICE MAKES *PURR*-FECT®

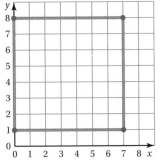

Check your answers at BigIdeasMath.com.

Find the distance between the points in the coordinate plane.

4. I and J

   _____

5. K and L

   _____

6. M and N

   _____

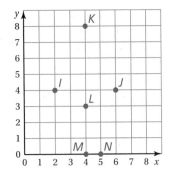

7. **BALANCE BEAMS** You walk once around a rectangular arrangement of balance beams. How far do you walk in feet?

   _____

Each unit represents 1 foot.

REVIEW: Line Graphs

Name _____

Key Concept and Vocabulary

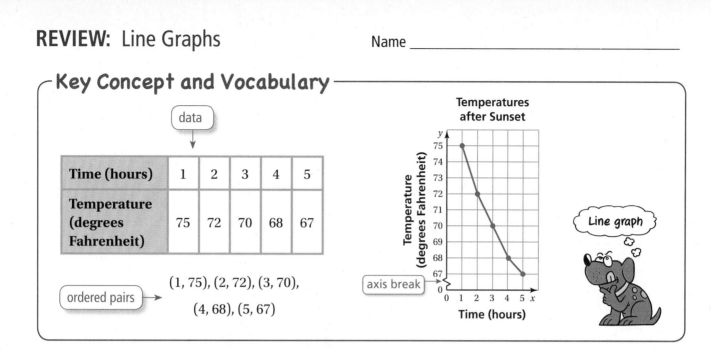

data

Time (hours)	1	2	3	4	5
Temperature (degrees Fahrenheit)	75	72	70	68	67

ordered pairs → (1, 75), (2, 72), (3, 70), (4, 68), (5, 67)

Temperatures after Sunset

axis break

Line graph

Skill Example

1. The table shows the total number of cans your class recycles over 5 days. Make a line graph of the data. Between which two days does your class recycle the most cans? Explain.

Day	0	1	2	3	4	5
Number of cans	0	10	30	60	85	120

Your class recycles the most cans between Days 4 and 5. The greatest difference in the number of cans occurs between the points (4, 85) and (5, 120).

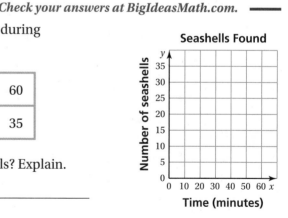

Cans Recycled

PRACTICE MAKES *PURR*-FECT®

Check your answers at BigIdeasMath.com.

2. The table shows the total numbers of seashells you find during an hour at the beach. Make a line graph of the data.

Time (minutes)	10	20	30	40	50	60
Number of seashells	5	15	20	25	32	35

Between which two times did you find the most seashells? Explain.

_____

_____

Estimate how many seashells you had after 15 minutes.

_____

Seashells Found

REVIEW: Writing Fractions

Name _____

Key Concept and Vocabulary

one-fourth

$\frac{1}{4}$ ← numerator

← denominator

Visual Model

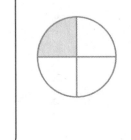

1 part shaded

4 equal parts in the whole

$\frac{1}{4}$

Skill Examples

1. 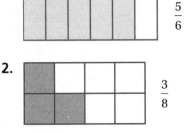 $\frac{5}{6}$

2. $\frac{3}{8}$

Application Example

3. What fraction of the Nigerian flag is green?

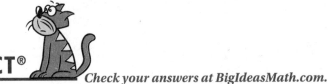

2 parts green

3 equal parts in the whole

∴ $\frac{2}{3}$ of the Nigerian flag is green.

PRACTICE MAKES *PURR-FECT*®

Check your answers at BigIdeasMath.com.

Write the fraction shown by the model.

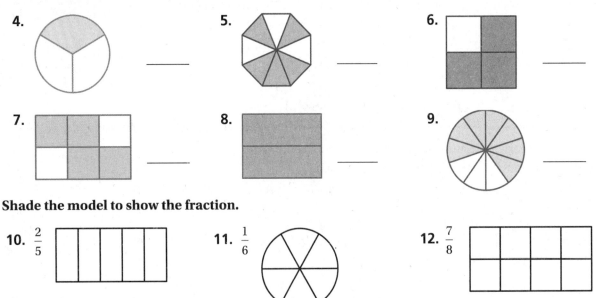

4. _____   5. _____   6. _____

7. _____   8. _____   9. _____

Shade the model to show the fraction.

10. $\frac{2}{5}$ 11. $\frac{1}{6}$ 12. $\frac{7}{8}$

13. **SANDWICH** A sandwich is cut into 4 equal pieces. You eat 1 piece. What fraction of the sandwich is *not* eaten? _____

14. **COLOR WHEEL** A color wheel is divided into equal parts. One part is yellow, 2 parts are red, 3 parts are green, and 4 parts are blue. What fraction of the color wheel is green? _____

Key Concept and Vocabulary

$$\frac{2}{3} = \frac{2 \times 4}{3 \times 4} = \frac{8}{12}$$

Multiply or divide the numerator and denominator by the same number.

$$\frac{8}{12} = \frac{8 \div 4}{12 \div 4} = \frac{2}{3}$$

Equivalent fractions

Visual Model

$\frac{2}{3}$

equivalent fractions

$\frac{8}{12}$

Skill Examples

1. $\dfrac{1}{2} = \dfrac{1 \times 2}{2 \times 2} = \dfrac{2}{4}$

2. $\dfrac{1}{2} = \dfrac{1 \times 3}{2 \times 3} = \dfrac{3}{6}$

$\frac{1}{2}, \frac{2}{4},$ and $\frac{3}{6}$ are all equivalent.

3. $\dfrac{15}{20} = \dfrac{15 \div 5}{20 \div 5} = \dfrac{3}{4}$

4. $\dfrac{63}{56} = \dfrac{63 \div 7}{56 \div 7} = \dfrac{9}{8}$

Application Example

5. A pizza has 12 pieces. Two-thirds of the pizza is left. How many pieces are left?

$$\frac{2}{3} = \frac{2 \times 4}{3 \times 4} = \frac{8}{12}$$

There are 8 pieces left.

PRACTICE MAKES *PURR*-FECT®

Check your answers at BigIdeasMath.com.

Find the equivalent fraction.

6. $\dfrac{1}{2} = \dfrac{\square}{8}$

7. $\dfrac{3}{5} = \dfrac{\square}{15}$

8. $\dfrac{4}{3} = \dfrac{\square}{9}$

9. $\dfrac{1}{3} = \dfrac{\square}{27}$

10. $\dfrac{8}{20} = \dfrac{\square}{5}$

11. $\dfrac{56}{64} = \dfrac{\square}{8}$

12. $\dfrac{6}{14} = \dfrac{3}{\square}$

13. $\dfrac{36}{16} = \dfrac{9}{\square}$

14. $\dfrac{1}{5} = \dfrac{10}{\square}$

15. $\dfrac{12}{36} = \dfrac{3}{\square}$

16. $\dfrac{7}{10} = \dfrac{14}{\square}$

17. $\dfrac{9}{24} = \dfrac{3}{\square}$

Shade the model so that the fraction is equivalent.

18. [model] = [model]

19. [model] = [model]

20. **PIZZA** A pizza has 12 pieces. Three-fourths of the pizza is left. How many pieces are left? _____

21. **SURVEY** A survey asked 240 people if they liked a movie. One-third liked it, one-sixth did not like it, and one-half had not seen it. How many people are in each of the three categories? _____

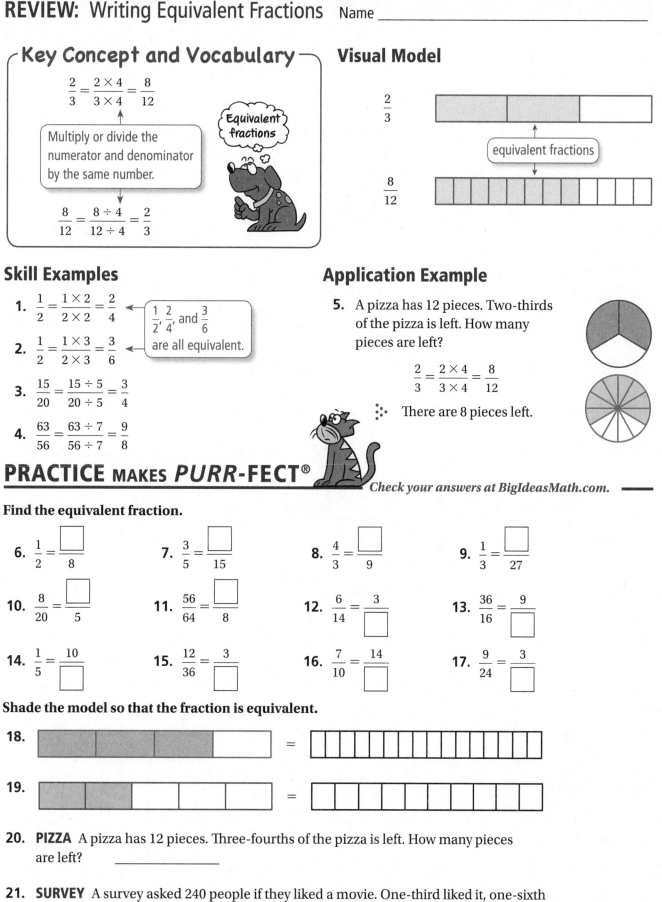

REVIEW: Simplifying Fractions

Name _____

Key Concept and Vocabulary

Divide the numerator and the denominator by a common factor.

$$\frac{8}{12} = \frac{8 \div 4}{12 \div 4} = \frac{2}{3}$$

Simplest form: The numerator and denominator have no common factors other than 1.

Simplifying fractions

Visual Model

unsimplified

$\frac{8}{12}$

simplified

$\frac{2}{3}$

Skill Examples

1. $\dfrac{2}{4} = \dfrac{2 \div 2}{4 \div 2} = \dfrac{1}{2}$

2. $\dfrac{3}{6} = \dfrac{3 \div 3}{6 \div 3} = \dfrac{1}{2}$

3. $\dfrac{15}{20} = \dfrac{15 \div 5}{20 \div 5} = \dfrac{3}{4}$

4. $\dfrac{80}{100} = \dfrac{80 \div 20}{100 \div 20} = \dfrac{4}{5}$

Application Example

5. Five of the 25 students in your class have a social media account. Write this fraction in simplest form.

   $$\frac{5}{25} = \frac{5 \div 5}{25 \div 5} = \frac{1}{5}$$

   5 5
   5   5
     5

   ∴ One-fifth of the students in your class have a social media account.

PRACTICE MAKES *PURR-FECT*®

Check your answers at BigIdeasMath.com.

Write the fraction in simplest form.

6. $\dfrac{16}{18} =$ _____

7. $\dfrac{10}{12} =$ _____

8. $\dfrac{6}{8} =$ _____

9. $\dfrac{15}{45} =$ _____

10. $\dfrac{12}{40} =$ _____

11. $\dfrac{14}{21} =$ _____

12. $\dfrac{6}{2} =$ _____

13. $\dfrac{20}{50} =$ _____

14. $\dfrac{24}{16} =$ _____

15. $\dfrac{20}{15} =$ _____

16. $\dfrac{55}{60} =$ _____

17. $\dfrac{21}{35} =$ _____

Shade the model so that the fraction is simplified.

18. _____ = _____

19. _____ = _____

20. **SOCIAL MEDIA** Eight of the 24 students in your class have a social media account. Write this fraction in simplest form. _____

21. **SIMPLIFYING** Write five different fractions that each simplify to $\dfrac{2}{5}$.

_____

REVIEW: Comparing and Ordering Fractions

Name _____

Key Concept and Vocabulary

$$\frac{2}{3} \ ? \ \frac{3}{4}$$

$$\frac{2}{3} = \frac{2 \times 4}{3 \times 4} = \frac{8}{12} \qquad \frac{3}{4} = \frac{3 \times 3}{4 \times 3} = \frac{9}{12}$$

Comparing fractions

Use a like denominator.

$$\frac{8}{12} < \frac{9}{12} \qquad \text{So, } \frac{2}{3} < \frac{3}{4}.$$

Visual Model

$\frac{2}{3}$

$\frac{3}{4}$

$$\frac{2}{3} < \frac{3}{4}$$

Skill Examples

1. $\frac{1}{2} > \frac{5}{12}$ because $\frac{1}{2} = \frac{6}{12}$, and $\frac{6}{12} > \frac{5}{12}$.

2. $\frac{3}{8} < \frac{2}{5}$ because $\frac{3}{8} = \frac{15}{40}, \frac{2}{5} = \frac{16}{40}$, and $\frac{15}{40} < \frac{16}{40}$.

3. Order from least to greatest: $\frac{3}{4}, \frac{3}{8}$, and $\frac{1}{8}$.

$\frac{1}{8}, \frac{3}{8}, \frac{3}{4}$ because $\frac{1}{8} < \frac{3}{8}, \frac{3}{4} = \frac{6}{8}$, and $\frac{6}{8} > \frac{3}{8}$.

Application Example

4. You run $\frac{7}{8}$ mile. Your friend runs $\frac{8}{10}$ mile. Who runs farther?

$\frac{7}{8} > \frac{8}{10}$ because $\frac{7}{8} = \frac{70}{80}, \frac{8}{10} = \frac{64}{80}$, and $\frac{70}{80} > \frac{64}{80}$.

∴ You run farther.

PRACTICE MAKES *PURR*-FECT®

Check your answers at BigIdeasMath.com.

Compare.

5. $\frac{4}{5} \ \square \ \frac{3}{5}$

6. $\frac{1}{2} \ \square \ \frac{1}{6}$

7. $\frac{3}{4} \ \square \ \frac{7}{8}$

8. $\frac{2}{3} \ \square \ \frac{5}{6}$

9. $\frac{1}{4} \ \square \ \frac{3}{10}$

10. $\frac{3}{9} \ \square \ \frac{1}{3}$

11. $\frac{7}{10} \ \square \ \frac{9}{20}$

12. $\frac{7}{12} \ \square \ \frac{3}{8}$

Order the fractions from least to greatest.

13. $\frac{5}{6}, \frac{1}{2}, \frac{5}{8}$ _____

14. $\frac{4}{5}, \frac{17}{20}, \frac{3}{4}$ _____

15. $\frac{2}{3}, \frac{7}{12}, \frac{3}{8}$ _____

16. $\frac{1}{3}, \frac{33}{100}, \frac{3}{5}$ _____

17. **PEANUTS** You have $\frac{4}{5}$ pound of peanuts. Your friend has $\frac{5}{6}$ pound of peanuts.

whose peanuts weigh more? _____

18. **ORDERING FRACTIONS** Graph the fractions on the number line and order them from least to greatest: $\frac{6}{8}, \frac{1}{4}, \frac{1}{3}$, and $\frac{5}{12}$.

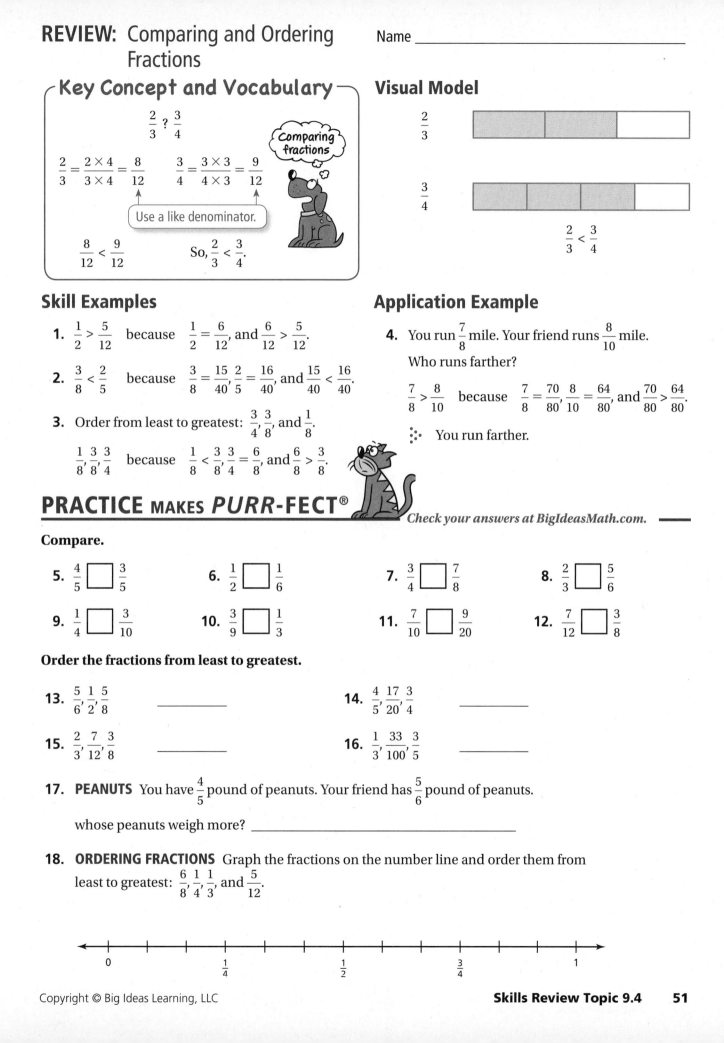

REVIEW: Estimating Fraction Sums and Differences

Name _____

Key Concept and Vocabulary

$$\frac{7}{8} + \frac{1}{6}$$

$$\downarrow \qquad \downarrow$$

$$1 + 0 = 1$$

Estimation

Use the benchmarks, 0, $\frac{1}{2}$, and 1 to round each fraction.

Visual Model

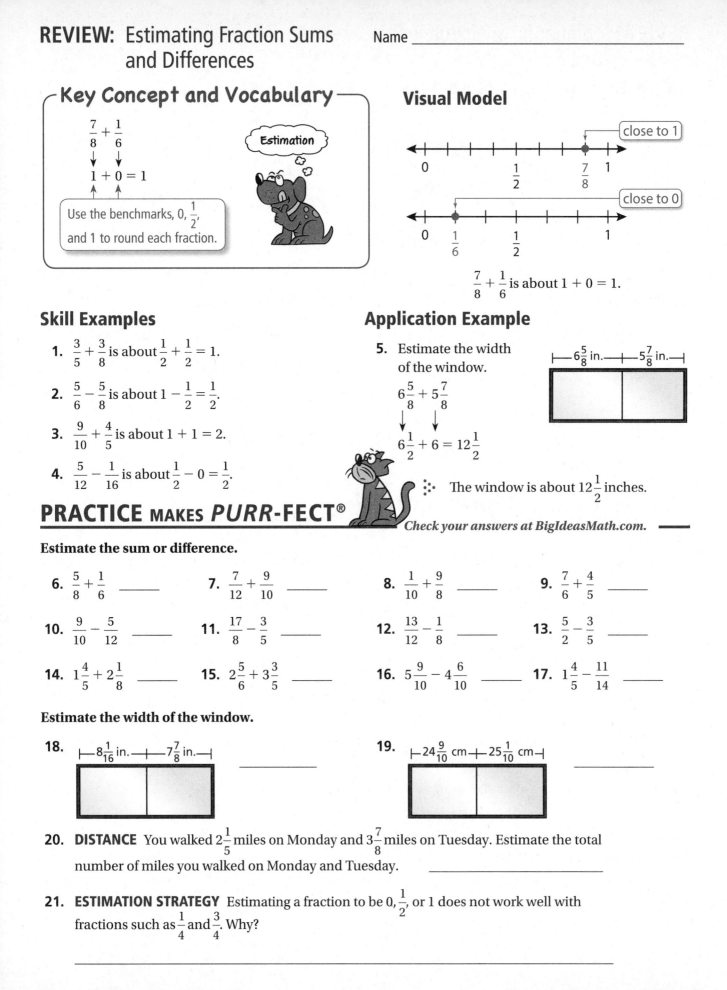

close to 1

0      $\frac{1}{2}$ $\frac{7}{8}$ 1

close to 0

0   $\frac{1}{6}$ $\frac{1}{2}$ 1

$\frac{7}{8} + \frac{1}{6}$ is about $1 + 0 = 1$.

Skill Examples

1. $\frac{3}{5} + \frac{3}{8}$ is about $\frac{1}{2} + \frac{1}{2} = 1$.

2. $\frac{5}{6} - \frac{5}{8}$ is about $1 - \frac{1}{2} = \frac{1}{2}$.

3. $\frac{9}{10} + \frac{4}{5}$ is about $1 + 1 = 2$.

4. $\frac{5}{12} - \frac{1}{16}$ is about $\frac{1}{2} - 0 = \frac{1}{2}$.

Application Example

5. Estimate the width of the window.

$$6\frac{5}{8} + 5\frac{7}{8}$$

$$\downarrow \qquad \downarrow$$

$$6\frac{1}{2} + 6 = 12\frac{1}{2}$$

$\vdots$ The window is about $12\frac{1}{2}$ inches.

$\vdash 6\frac{5}{8}$ in. $\dashv$ $5\frac{7}{8}$ in. $\dashv$

PRACTICE MAKES *PURR*-FECT®

Check your answers at BigIdeasMath.com.

Estimate the sum or difference.

6. $\frac{5}{8} + \frac{1}{6}$ _____

7. $\frac{7}{12} + \frac{9}{10}$ _____

8. $\frac{1}{10} + \frac{9}{8}$ _____

9. $\frac{7}{6} + \frac{4}{5}$ _____

10. $\frac{9}{10} - \frac{5}{12}$ _____

11. $\frac{17}{8} - \frac{3}{5}$ _____

12. $\frac{13}{12} - \frac{1}{8}$ _____

13. $\frac{5}{2} - \frac{3}{5}$ _____

14. $1\frac{4}{5} + 2\frac{1}{8}$ _____

15. $2\frac{5}{6} + 3\frac{3}{5}$ _____

16. $5\frac{9}{10} - 4\frac{6}{10}$ _____

17. $1\frac{4}{5} - \frac{11}{14}$ _____

Estimate the width of the window.

18. $\vdash 8\frac{1}{16}$ in. $\dashv$ $7\frac{7}{8}$ in. $\dashv$ _____

19. $\vdash 24\frac{9}{10}$ cm $\dashv$ $25\frac{1}{10}$ cm $\dashv$ _____

20. **DISTANCE** You walked $2\frac{1}{5}$ miles on Monday and $3\frac{7}{8}$ miles on Tuesday. Estimate the total number of miles you walked on Monday and Tuesday. _____

21. **ESTIMATION STRATEGY** Estimating a fraction to be 0, $\frac{1}{2}$, or 1 does not work well with fractions such as $\frac{1}{4}$ and $\frac{3}{4}$. Why?

_____

REVIEW: Adding and Subtracting Fractions with Like Denominators

Name _____

Key Concept and Vocabulary

$$\frac{2}{5} + \frac{1}{5} = \frac{2+1}{5} = \frac{3}{5}$$

Like denominators

Add or subtract numerators.

$$\frac{3}{5} - \frac{1}{5} = \frac{3-1}{5} = \frac{2}{5}$$

Visual Models

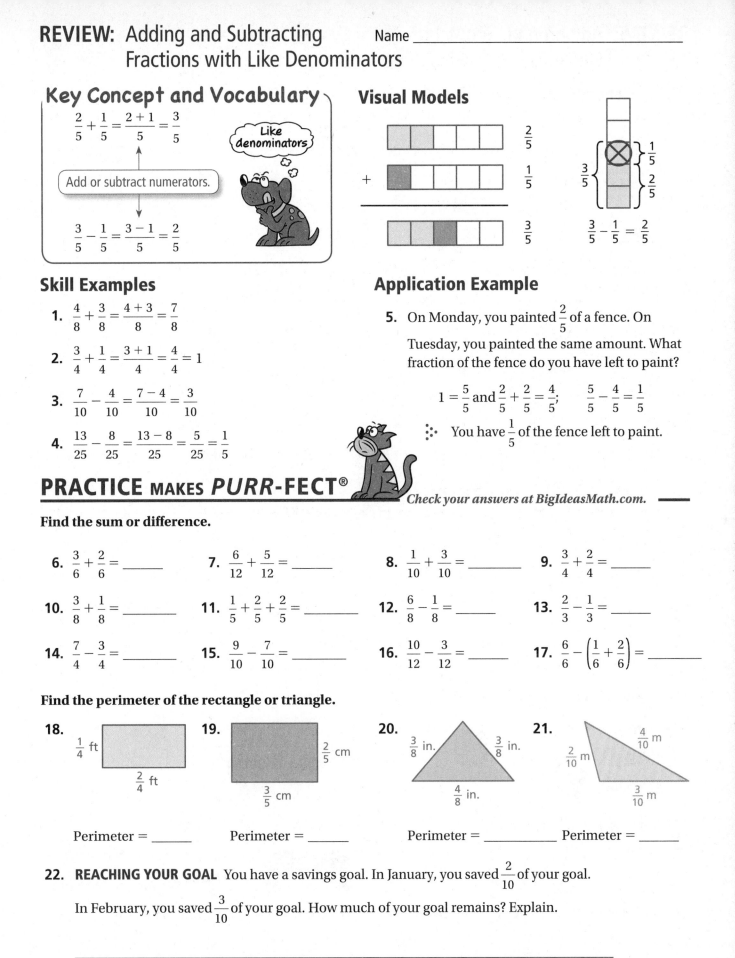

$$\frac{2}{5}$$

$$+ \quad \frac{1}{5}$$

$$\frac{3}{5}$$

$$\frac{3}{5} \left\{ \begin{array}{l} \frac{1}{5} \\ \frac{2}{5} \end{array} \right.$$

$$\frac{3}{5} - \frac{1}{5} = \frac{2}{5}$$

Skill Examples

1. $\dfrac{4}{8} + \dfrac{3}{8} = \dfrac{4+3}{8} = \dfrac{7}{8}$

2. $\dfrac{3}{4} + \dfrac{1}{4} = \dfrac{3+1}{4} = \dfrac{4}{4} = 1$

3. $\dfrac{7}{10} - \dfrac{4}{10} = \dfrac{7-4}{10} = \dfrac{3}{10}$

4. $\dfrac{13}{25} - \dfrac{8}{25} = \dfrac{13-8}{25} = \dfrac{5}{25} = \dfrac{1}{5}$

Application Example

5. On Monday, you painted $\dfrac{2}{5}$ of a fence. On Tuesday, you painted the same amount. What fraction of the fence do you have left to paint?

$$1 = \frac{5}{5} \text{ and } \frac{2}{5} + \frac{2}{5} = \frac{4}{5}; \qquad \frac{5}{5} - \frac{4}{5} = \frac{1}{5}$$

You have $\dfrac{1}{5}$ of the fence left to paint.

PRACTICE MAKES PURR-FECT®

Check your answers at BigIdeasMath.com.

Find the sum or difference.

6. $\dfrac{3}{6} + \dfrac{2}{6} = $ _____

7. $\dfrac{6}{12} + \dfrac{5}{12} = $ _____

8. $\dfrac{1}{10} + \dfrac{3}{10} = $ _____

9. $\dfrac{3}{4} + \dfrac{2}{4} = $ _____

10. $\dfrac{3}{8} + \dfrac{1}{8} = $ _____

11. $\dfrac{1}{5} + \dfrac{2}{5} + \dfrac{2}{5} = $ _____

12. $\dfrac{6}{8} - \dfrac{1}{8} = $ _____

13. $\dfrac{2}{3} - \dfrac{1}{3} = $ _____

14. $\dfrac{7}{4} - \dfrac{3}{4} = $ _____

15. $\dfrac{9}{10} - \dfrac{7}{10} = $ _____

16. $\dfrac{10}{12} - \dfrac{3}{12} = $ _____

17. $\dfrac{6}{6} - \left(\dfrac{1}{6} + \dfrac{2}{6} \right) = $ _____

Find the perimeter of the rectangle or triangle.

18. $\frac{1}{4}$ ft, $\frac{2}{4}$ ft

Perimeter = _____

19. $\frac{2}{5}$ cm, $\frac{3}{5}$ cm

Perimeter = _____

20. $\frac{3}{8}$ in., $\frac{3}{8}$ in., $\frac{4}{8}$ in.

Perimeter = _____

21. $\frac{4}{10}$ m, $\frac{2}{10}$ m, $\frac{3}{10}$ m

Perimeter = _____

22. **REACHING YOUR GOAL** You have a savings goal. In January, you saved $\dfrac{2}{10}$ of your goal.

In February, you saved $\dfrac{3}{10}$ of your goal. How much of your goal remains? Explain.

_____

Key Concept and Vocabulary

$$\frac{1}{2} + \frac{1}{3} = \frac{3}{6} + \frac{2}{6} = \frac{5}{6}$$

Use a like denominator.

$$\frac{1}{2} - \frac{1}{3} = \frac{3}{6} - \frac{2}{6} = \frac{1}{6}$$

Unlike denominators

Visual Models

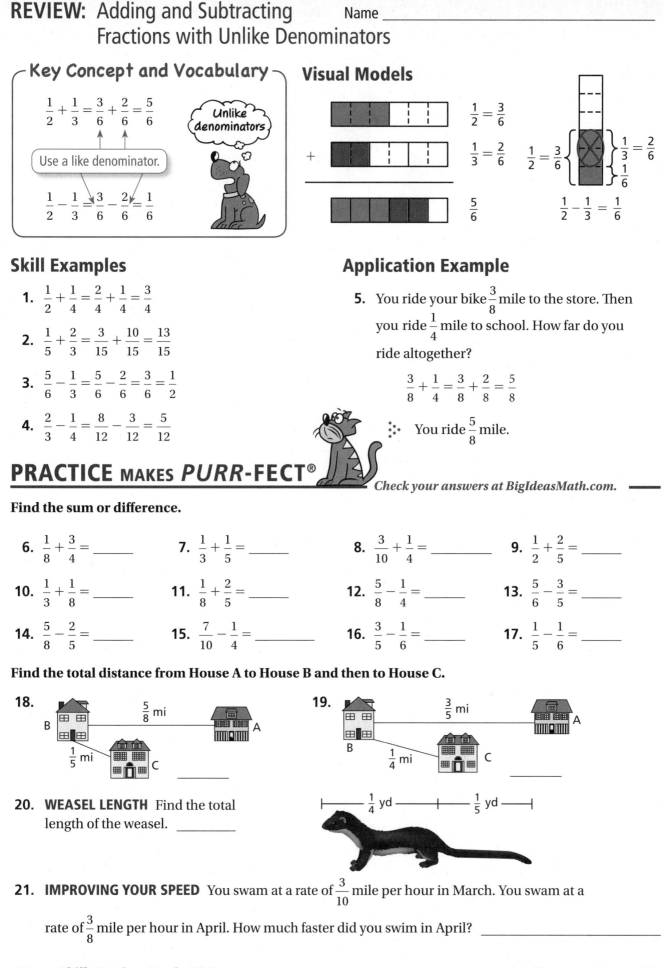

$$\frac{1}{2} = \frac{3}{6}$$

$$\frac{1}{3} = \frac{2}{6}$$

$$\frac{5}{6}$$

$$\frac{1}{2} = \frac{3}{6} \left\{ \begin{array}{l} \frac{1}{3} = \frac{2}{6} \\ \frac{1}{6} \end{array} \right.$$

$$\frac{1}{2} - \frac{1}{3} = \frac{1}{6}$$

Skill Examples

1. $\frac{1}{2} + \frac{1}{4} = \frac{2}{4} + \frac{1}{4} = \frac{3}{4}$

2. $\frac{1}{5} + \frac{2}{3} = \frac{3}{15} + \frac{10}{15} = \frac{13}{15}$

3. $\frac{5}{6} - \frac{1}{3} = \frac{5}{6} - \frac{2}{6} = \frac{3}{6} = \frac{1}{2}$

4. $\frac{2}{3} - \frac{1}{4} = \frac{8}{12} - \frac{3}{12} = \frac{5}{12}$

Application Example

5. You ride your bike $\frac{3}{8}$ mile to the store. Then you ride $\frac{1}{4}$ mile to school. How far do you ride altogether?

$$\frac{3}{8} + \frac{1}{4} = \frac{3}{8} + \frac{2}{8} = \frac{5}{8}$$

∴ You ride $\frac{5}{8}$ mile.

PRACTICE MAKES *PURR*-FECT®

Check your answers at BigIdeasMath.com.

Find the sum or difference.

6. $\frac{1}{8} + \frac{3}{4} =$ _____

7. $\frac{1}{3} + \frac{1}{5} =$ _____

8. $\frac{3}{10} + \frac{1}{4} =$ _____

9. $\frac{1}{2} + \frac{2}{5} =$ _____

10. $\frac{1}{3} + \frac{1}{8} =$ _____

11. $\frac{1}{8} + \frac{2}{5} =$ _____

12. $\frac{5}{8} - \frac{1}{4} =$ _____

13. $\frac{5}{6} - \frac{3}{5} =$ _____

14. $\frac{5}{8} - \frac{2}{5} =$ _____

15. $\frac{7}{10} - \frac{1}{4} =$ _____

16. $\frac{3}{5} - \frac{1}{6} =$ _____

17. $\frac{1}{5} - \frac{1}{6} =$ _____

Find the total distance from House A to House B and then to House C.

18. $\frac{5}{8}$ mi   B   A $\frac{1}{5}$ mi   C _____

19. $\frac{3}{5}$ mi   A   B $\frac{1}{4}$ mi   C _____

20. WEASEL LENGTH Find the total length of the weasel. _____

$\frac{1}{4}$ yd $\frac{1}{5}$ yd

21. IMPROVING YOUR SPEED You swam at a rate of $\frac{3}{10}$ mile per hour in March. You swam at a rate of $\frac{3}{8}$ mile per hour in April. How much faster did you swim in April? _____

REVIEW: Multiplying Whole Numbers and Fractions

Name _____

Key Concept and Vocabulary

Multiply whole number and numerator.

$$3 \times \frac{2}{5} = \frac{3 \times 2}{5} = \frac{6}{5}$$

Multiply whole numbers and fractions.

Visual Model

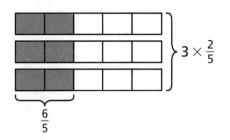

$3 \times \frac{2}{5}$

$\frac{6}{5}$

Skill Examples

1. $4 \times \frac{2}{3} = \frac{4 \times 2}{3} = \frac{8}{3}$

2. $5 \times \frac{1}{6} = \frac{5 \times 1}{6} = \frac{5}{6}$

3. $2 \times \frac{3}{4} = \frac{2 \times 3}{4} = \frac{6}{4} = \frac{3}{2}$

4. $8 \times \frac{5}{10} = \frac{8 \times 5}{10} = \frac{40}{10} = 4$

Application Example

5. One lap around a track is equal to $\frac{4}{5}$ mile. You walk 3 laps around the track. How many miles do you walk?

$$3 \times \frac{4}{5} = \frac{3 \times 4}{5} = \frac{12}{5}$$

You walk $\frac{12}{5}$ miles.

PRACTICE MAKES *PURR*-FECT®

Check your answers at BigIdeasMath.com.

Find the product.

6. $3 \times \frac{1}{4} =$ _____

7. $1 \times \frac{5}{8} =$ _____

8. $5 \times \frac{2}{3} =$ _____

9. $2 \times \frac{2}{5} =$ _____

10. $4 \times \frac{7}{10} =$ _____

11. $8 \times \frac{3}{4} =$ _____

12. $3 \times \frac{4}{3} =$ _____

13. $6 \times \frac{7}{12} =$ _____

14. $\frac{3}{2} \times 5 =$ _____

15. $\frac{9}{10} \times 9 =$ _____

16. $3 \times 2 \times \frac{4}{5} =$ _____

17. $4 \times \frac{5}{12} \times 6 =$ _____

Compare.

18. $4 \times \frac{7}{8}$ ☐ $6 \times \frac{3}{8}$

19. $\frac{4}{5} \times 3$ ☐ $\frac{3}{10} \times 9$

20. $\frac{4}{3} \times 9$ ☐ $8 \times \frac{3}{2}$

21. **CINNAMON** A recipe calls for $\frac{3}{4}$ teaspoon of cinnamon. You make 3 batches of the recipe.

How may teaspoons of cinnamon do you use? _____

22. **PIANO PRACTICE** You spend $\frac{5}{2}$ hours practicing the piano each day for 3 days. Your friend spends $\frac{4}{3}$ hours practicing the piano each day for 4 days. Who spends more time practicing the piano? _____

REVIEW: Multiplying Fractions

Name _____

Key Concept and Vocabulary

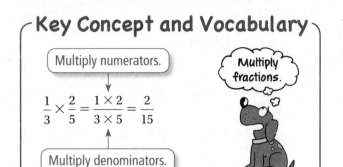

Multiply numerators.

$$\frac{1}{3} \times \frac{2}{5} = \frac{1 \times 2}{3 \times 5} = \frac{2}{15}$$

Multiply denominators.

Multiply fractions.

Visual Model

2 out of 15 parts are shaded twice.

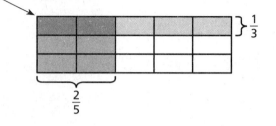

$\frac{1}{3}$

$\frac{2}{5}$

Skill Examples

1. $\dfrac{2}{3} \times \dfrac{1}{4} = \dfrac{2 \times 1}{3 \times 4} = \dfrac{2}{12} = \dfrac{1}{6}$

2. $\dfrac{3}{8} \times \dfrac{4}{5} = \dfrac{3 \times 4}{8 \times 5} = \dfrac{12}{40} = \dfrac{3}{10}$

3. $\dfrac{2}{5} \times \dfrac{1}{4} = \dfrac{2 \times 1}{5 \times 4} = \dfrac{2}{20} = \dfrac{1}{10}$

4. $\dfrac{5}{6} \times \dfrac{3}{4} = \dfrac{5 \times 3}{6 \times 4} = \dfrac{15}{24} = \dfrac{5}{8}$

Application Example

5. A recipe calls for $\dfrac{3}{4}$ cup of flour. You want to make $\dfrac{1}{2}$ of the recipe. How much flour do you need?

$$\frac{1}{2} \times \frac{3}{4} = \frac{1 \times 3}{2 \times 4} = \frac{3}{8}$$

You need $\dfrac{3}{8}$ cup flour.

PRACTICE MAKES PURR-FECT®

Check your answers at BigIdeasMath.com.

Find the product.

6. $\dfrac{1}{3} \times \dfrac{3}{8} =$ _____

7. $\dfrac{1}{2} \times \dfrac{1}{4} =$ _____

8. $\dfrac{1}{10} \times \dfrac{3}{10} =$ _____

9. $\dfrac{3}{2} \times \dfrac{2}{5} =$ _____

10. $\dfrac{3}{8} \times \dfrac{1}{2} =$ _____

11. $\dfrac{1}{5} \times \dfrac{2}{5} =$ _____

12. $\dfrac{2}{3} \times \dfrac{2}{3} =$ _____

13. $\dfrac{3}{2} \times \dfrac{2}{3} =$ _____

14. $\dfrac{3}{1} \times \dfrac{1}{3} =$ _____

15. $\dfrac{5}{12} \times \dfrac{5}{2} =$ _____

16. $\dfrac{15}{8} \times \dfrac{6}{5} =$ _____

17. $\dfrac{1}{3} \times \dfrac{3}{4} \times \dfrac{4}{5} =$ _____

Find the area of the rectangle.

18. $\dfrac{1}{2}$ ft $\dfrac{1}{2}$ ft

Area = _____

19. $\dfrac{3}{10}$ cm $\dfrac{1}{2}$ cm

Area = _____

20. $\dfrac{3}{8}$ in. $\dfrac{5}{8}$ in.

Area = _____

21. $\dfrac{2}{5}$ m $\dfrac{3}{5}$ m

Area = _____

22. **OPEN-ENDED** Find three different pairs of fractions that have the same product.

☐ · ☐ = ☐   ☐ · ☐ = ☐   ☐ · ☐ = ☐

Name _____

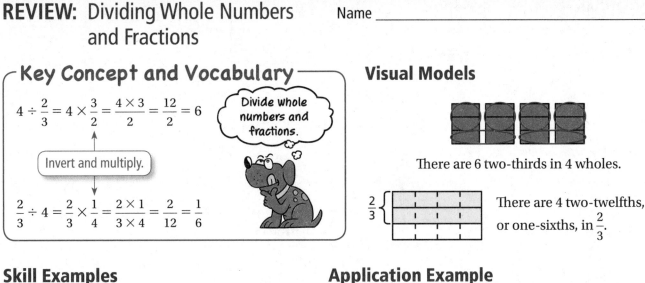

Key Concept and Vocabulary

$$4 \div \frac{2}{3} = 4 \times \frac{3}{2} = \frac{4 \times 3}{2} = \frac{12}{2} = 6$$

Invert and multiply.

$$\frac{2}{3} \div 4 = \frac{2}{3} \times \frac{1}{4} = \frac{2 \times 1}{3 \times 4} = \frac{2}{12} = \frac{1}{6}$$

Divide whole numbers and fractions.

Visual Models

There are 6 two-thirds in 4 wholes.

$\frac{2}{3}$ { There are 4 two-twelfths, or one-sixths, in $\frac{2}{3}$.

Skill Examples

1. $2 \div \frac{4}{5} = 2 \times \frac{5}{4} = \frac{2 \times 5}{4} = \frac{10}{4} = \frac{5}{2}$

2. $4 \div \frac{1}{2} = 4 \times 2 = 8$

3. $\frac{3}{4} \div 3 = \frac{3}{4} \times \frac{1}{3} = \frac{3 \times 1}{4 \times 3} = \frac{3}{12} = \frac{1}{4}$

4. $\frac{1}{3} \div 5 = \frac{1}{3} \times \frac{1}{5} = \frac{1 \times 1}{3 \times 5} = \frac{1}{15}$

Application Example

5. You have $\frac{1}{2}$ gallon of milk. You pour the milk equally into 8 glasses. How much milk is in each glass?

$$\frac{1}{2} \div 8 = \frac{1}{2} \times \frac{1}{8} = \frac{1 \times 1}{2 \times 8} = \frac{1}{16}$$

There is $\frac{1}{16}$ gallon of milk in each glass.

PRACTICE MAKES *PURR*-FECT®

Check your answers at BigIdeasMath.com.

Find the quotient.

6. $2 \div \frac{1}{5} =$ _____

7. $3 \div \frac{1}{2} =$ _____

8. $6 \div \frac{3}{4} =$ _____

9. $4 \div \frac{5}{6} =$ _____

10. $6 \div \frac{4}{5} =$ _____

11. $10 \div \frac{3}{8} =$ _____

12. $\frac{1}{4} \div 3 =$ _____

13. $\frac{1}{3} \div 2 =$ _____

14. $\frac{5}{8} \div 5 =$ _____

15. $\frac{3}{5} \div 6 =$ _____

16. $\frac{3}{4} \div 7 =$ _____

17. $\frac{4}{5} \div 10 =$ _____

Compare.

18. $5 \div \frac{1}{4} \;\boxed{}\; 4 \div \frac{1}{5}$

19. $\frac{7}{8} \div 6 \;\boxed{}\; \frac{7}{8} \div 8$

20. $2 \div \frac{3}{2} \;\boxed{}\; 3 \div \frac{2}{3}$

21. **SMOOTHIES** You need $\frac{3}{4}$ cup of strawberries to make a smoothie. How many smoothies can you make with 3 cups of strawberries? _____

22. **WATERING PLANTS** You have 5 gallons of water. You use $\frac{1}{2}$ of the water to water a tree. Then you divide the rest of the water equally among 10 plants. How much water does each plant get? _____

Key Concept and Vocabulary

$$\frac{2}{3} \div \frac{1}{2} = \frac{2}{3} \times \frac{2}{1} = \frac{2 \times 2}{3 \times 1} = \frac{4}{3}$$

Invert and multiply.

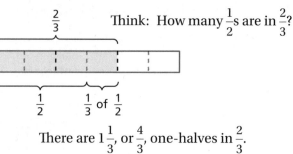

Divide fractions.

Visual Model

Think: How many $\frac{1}{2}$s are in $\frac{2}{3}$?

$\frac{2}{3}$

$\frac{1}{2}$ $\frac{1}{3}$ of $\frac{1}{2}$

There are $1\frac{1}{3}$, or $\frac{4}{3}$, one-halves in $\frac{2}{3}$.

Skill Examples

1. $\dfrac{2}{5} \div \dfrac{1}{5} = \dfrac{2}{5} \times \dfrac{5}{1} = \dfrac{2 \times 5}{5 \times 1} = \dfrac{10}{5} = 2$

2. $\dfrac{9}{4} \div \dfrac{3}{4} = \dfrac{9}{4} \times \dfrac{4}{3} = \dfrac{9 \times 4}{4 \times 3} = \dfrac{36}{12} = 3$

3. $\dfrac{1}{6} \div \dfrac{2}{3} = \dfrac{1}{6} \times \dfrac{3}{2} = \dfrac{1 \times 3}{6 \times 2} = \dfrac{3}{12} = \dfrac{1}{4}$

4. $\dfrac{3}{4} \div \dfrac{5}{12} = \dfrac{3}{4} \times \dfrac{12}{5} = \dfrac{3 \times 12}{4 \times 5} = \dfrac{36}{20} = \dfrac{9}{5}$

Application Example

5. There are $\frac{3}{2}$ cups of trail mix in a bag. A serving of trail mix is $\frac{1}{4}$ cup. How many servings of trail mix are in the bag?

$$\frac{3}{2} \div \frac{1}{4} = \frac{3}{2} \times \frac{4}{1} = \frac{3 \times 4}{2 \times 1} = \frac{12}{2} = 6$$

There are 6 servings of trail mix in the bag.

PRACTICE MAKES *PURR*-FECT®

Check your answers at BigIdeasMath.com.

Find the quotient.

6. $\dfrac{3}{5} \div \dfrac{1}{5} =$ _____

7. $\dfrac{1}{2} \div \dfrac{1}{8} =$ _____

8. $\dfrac{2}{3} \div \dfrac{1}{6} =$ _____

9. $\dfrac{1}{5} \div \dfrac{2}{3} =$ _____

10. $\dfrac{2}{3} \div \dfrac{3}{4} =$ _____

11. $\dfrac{4}{5} \div \dfrac{3}{10} =$ _____

12. $\dfrac{3}{8} \div \dfrac{3}{8} =$ _____

13. $\dfrac{1}{3} \div \dfrac{5}{6} =$ _____

14. $\dfrac{2}{3} \div \dfrac{2}{9} =$ _____

15. $\dfrac{9}{4} \div \dfrac{1}{4} =$ _____

16. $\dfrac{3}{4} \div \dfrac{2}{3} =$ _____

17. $\dfrac{7}{10} \div \dfrac{3}{8} =$ _____

Find the unknown measure of the rectangle.

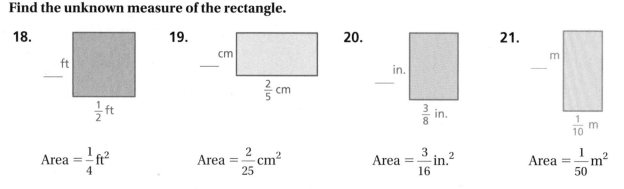

18. ___ ft, $\frac{1}{2}$ ft, Area $= \dfrac{1}{4}$ ft^2

19. ___ cm, $\frac{2}{5}$ cm, Area $= \dfrac{2}{25}$ cm^2

20. ___ in., $\frac{3}{8}$ in., Area $= \dfrac{3}{16}$ in.^{2}

21. ___ m, $\frac{1}{10}$ m, Area $= \dfrac{1}{50}$ m^2

22. **MAGNETIC TAPE** A refrigerator magnet uses $\frac{5}{8}$ inch of magnetic tape. How many refrigerator magnets can you make with $9\frac{3}{8}$ inches of magnetic tape? Explain.

REVIEW: Evaluating Complex Fractions

Name _____

Key Concept and Vocabulary

A complex fraction is a fraction that contains a fraction in its numerator, denominator, or both. To simplify a complex fraction, divide its numerator by its denominator.

Complex fractions

Algebra: $\dfrac{\frac{a}{b}}{\frac{c}{d}} = \dfrac{a}{b} \div \dfrac{c}{d} = \dfrac{a}{b} \cdot \dfrac{d}{c}$, where $b, c, d \neq 0$

Numbers: $\dfrac{\frac{2}{3}}{\frac{5}{6}} = \dfrac{2}{3} \div \dfrac{5}{6} = \dfrac{2}{3} \cdot \dfrac{6}{5} = \dfrac{12}{15} = \dfrac{4}{5}$

Skill Examples

1. $\dfrac{\frac{5}{8}}{4} = \dfrac{5}{8} \div 4 = \dfrac{5}{8} \cdot \dfrac{1}{4} = \dfrac{5}{32}$

2. $\dfrac{15}{\frac{9}{10}} = 15 \div \dfrac{9}{10} = \dfrac{15}{1} \cdot \dfrac{10}{9} = \dfrac{150}{9} = \dfrac{50}{3}$

3. $\dfrac{\frac{1}{3}}{\frac{5}{7}} = \dfrac{1}{3} \div \dfrac{5}{7} = \dfrac{1}{3} \cdot \dfrac{7}{5} = \dfrac{7}{15}$

4. $\dfrac{\frac{9}{16}}{\frac{3}{8}} = \dfrac{9}{16} \div \dfrac{3}{8} = \dfrac{9}{16} \cdot \dfrac{8}{3} = \dfrac{72}{48} = \dfrac{3}{2}$

PRACTICE MAKES PURR-FECT®

Check your answers at BigIdeasMath.com.

Simplify the complex fraction.

5. $\dfrac{\frac{3}{2}}{6} = $ _____

6. $\dfrac{20}{\frac{4}{5}} = $ _____

7. $\dfrac{\frac{9}{2}}{\frac{12}{7}} = $ _____

8. $\dfrac{\frac{7}{10}}{\frac{9}{20}} = $ _____

9. $\dfrac{\frac{2}{3}}{\frac{16}{27}} = $ _____

10. $\dfrac{5}{\frac{7}{10}} = $ _____

11. $\dfrac{\frac{12}{17}}{8} = $ _____

12. $\dfrac{\frac{3}{14}}{\frac{13}{49}} = $ _____

13. $\dfrac{\frac{27}{32}}{\frac{7}{8}} = $ _____

14. $\dfrac{\frac{9}{10}}{3} = $ _____

15. $\dfrac{6}{\frac{1}{6}} = $ _____

16. $\dfrac{\frac{4}{5}}{\frac{22}{25}} = $ _____

17. $\dfrac{24}{\frac{18}{7}} = $ _____

18. $\dfrac{\frac{1}{4}}{\frac{1}{10}} = $ _____

19. $\dfrac{\frac{3}{5}}{16} = $ _____

20. $\dfrac{\frac{16}{21}}{\frac{8}{9}} = $ _____

Key Concept and Vocabulary

improper fraction: a fraction greater than 1

$$\frac{5}{2} = 2\frac{1}{2}$$

mixed number: represents the sum of a whole number and a proper fraction

Mixed numbers

Visual Model

$$\frac{2}{2} = 1 \qquad \frac{2}{2} = 1 \qquad \frac{1}{2}$$

$$\frac{5}{2}$$

Skill Examples

1. $\frac{7}{3} = \frac{3}{3} + \frac{3}{3} + \frac{1}{3} = 2\frac{1}{3}$

2. $\frac{8}{4} = \frac{4}{4} + \frac{4}{4} = 2$

3. $2\frac{1}{4} = \frac{8}{4} + \frac{1}{4} = \frac{9}{4}$

4. $3\frac{3}{5} = \frac{15}{5} + \frac{3}{5} = \frac{18}{5}$

Application Example

5. You fill a half-gallon container with water 13 times. How many gallons of water do you use?

| 13 halves | $\frac{13}{2} = 6\frac{1}{2}$ | 6 and one-half |

You use $6\frac{1}{2}$ gallons of water.

PRACTICE MAKES *PURR*-FECT®

Check your answers at BigIdeasMath.com.

Write the improper fraction as a mixed number.

6. $\frac{4}{3} =$ _____

7. $\frac{3}{2} =$ _____

8. $\frac{8}{3} =$ _____

9. $\frac{9}{6} =$ _____

10. $\frac{7}{4} =$ _____

11. $\frac{28}{3} =$ _____

12. $\frac{19}{4} =$ _____

13. $\frac{11}{2} =$ _____

Write the mixed number as an improper fraction.

14. $2\frac{2}{3} =$ _____

15. $5\frac{1}{4} =$ _____

16. $3\frac{2}{5} =$ _____

17. $1\frac{3}{8} =$ _____

18. Rewrite the sentence using a mixed number: Susan drinks $\frac{5}{4}$ quarts of milk.

_____

19. Rewrite the sentence using an improper fraction: Tom runs for $2\frac{1}{4}$ hours.

_____

20. **NUMBER LINE** Plot the improper fractions on the number line: $\frac{7}{4}, \frac{7}{2},$ and $\frac{19}{4}$.

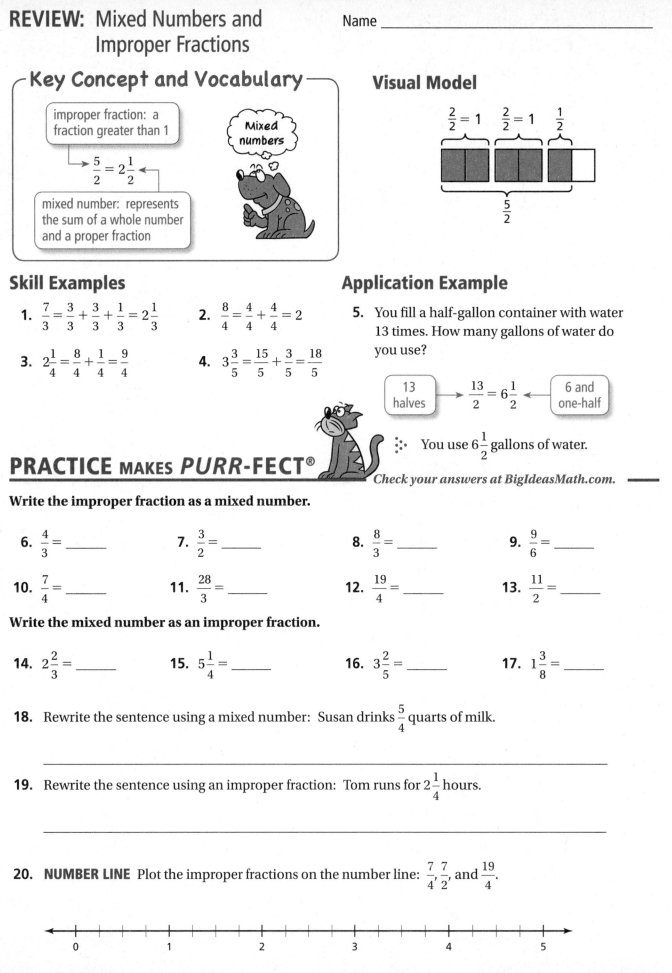

REVIEW: Adding and Subtracting Mixed Numbers

Name _____

Key Concept and Vocabulary

$$2\frac{2}{3} + 1\frac{2}{3} = (2+1) + \left(\frac{2}{3} + \frac{2}{3}\right)$$

$$= 3\frac{4}{3} = 4\frac{1}{3}$$

$$5\frac{1}{5} - 1\frac{3}{5} = 4\frac{6}{5} - 1\frac{3}{5}$$

$$= (4-1) + \left(\frac{6}{5} - \frac{3}{5}\right) = 3\frac{3}{5}$$

Add and subtract.

Visual Models

$2\frac{2}{3}$ $1\frac{2}{3}$ $4\frac{1}{3}$

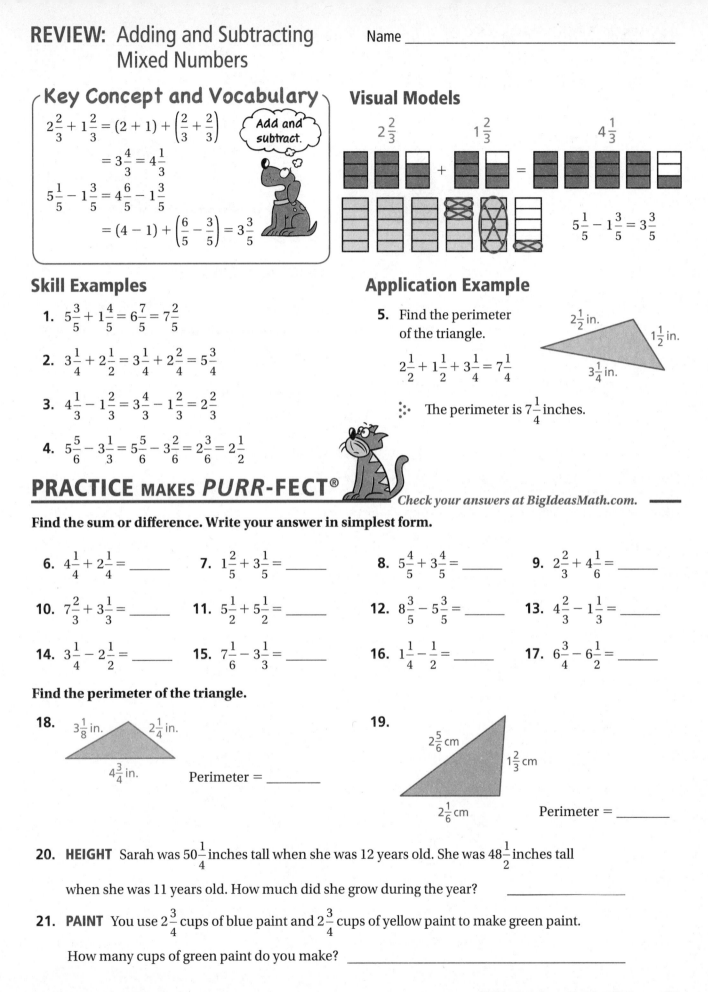

$$5\frac{1}{5} - 1\frac{3}{5} = 3\frac{3}{5}$$

Skill Examples

1. $5\frac{3}{5} + 1\frac{4}{5} = 6\frac{7}{5} = 7\frac{2}{5}$

2. $3\frac{1}{4} + 2\frac{1}{2} = 3\frac{1}{4} + 2\frac{2}{4} = 5\frac{3}{4}$

3. $4\frac{1}{3} - 1\frac{2}{3} = 3\frac{4}{3} - 1\frac{2}{3} = 2\frac{2}{3}$

4. $5\frac{5}{6} - 3\frac{1}{3} = 5\frac{5}{6} - 3\frac{2}{6} = 2\frac{3}{6} = 2\frac{1}{2}$

Application Example

5. Find the perimeter of the triangle.

$$2\frac{1}{2} + 1\frac{1}{2} + 3\frac{1}{4} = 7\frac{1}{4}$$

$2\frac{1}{2}$ in. $1\frac{1}{2}$ in. $3\frac{1}{4}$ in.

⋮⋅ The perimeter is $7\frac{1}{4}$ inches.

PRACTICE MAKES PURR-FECT®

Check your answers at BigIdeasMath.com.

Find the sum or difference. Write your answer in simplest form.

6. $4\frac{1}{4} + 2\frac{1}{4} =$ _____

7. $1\frac{2}{5} + 3\frac{1}{5} =$ _____

8. $5\frac{4}{5} + 3\frac{4}{5} =$ _____

9. $2\frac{2}{3} + 4\frac{1}{6} =$ _____

10. $7\frac{2}{3} + 3\frac{1}{3} =$ _____

11. $5\frac{1}{2} + 5\frac{1}{2} =$ _____

12. $8\frac{3}{5} - 5\frac{3}{5} =$ _____

13. $4\frac{2}{3} - 1\frac{1}{3} =$ _____

14. $3\frac{1}{4} - 2\frac{1}{2} =$ _____

15. $7\frac{1}{6} - 3\frac{1}{3} =$ _____

16. $1\frac{1}{4} - \frac{1}{2} =$ _____

17. $6\frac{3}{4} - 6\frac{1}{2} =$ _____

Find the perimeter of the triangle.

18.

$3\frac{1}{8}$ in. $2\frac{1}{4}$ in.

$4\frac{3}{4}$ in.

Perimeter = _____

19.

$2\frac{5}{6}$ cm $1\frac{2}{3}$ cm

$2\frac{1}{6}$ cm

Perimeter = _____

20. HEIGHT Sarah was $50\frac{1}{4}$ inches tall when she was 12 years old. She was $48\frac{1}{2}$ inches tall when she was 11 years old. How much did she grow during the year? _____

21. PAINT You use $2\frac{3}{4}$ cups of blue paint and $2\frac{3}{4}$ cups of yellow paint to make green paint. How many cups of green paint do you make? _____

REVIEW: Multiplying Mixed Numbers   Name _____

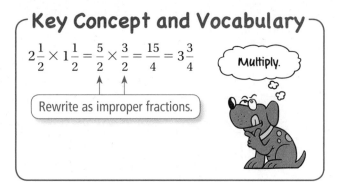

Key Concept and Vocabulary

$2\frac{1}{2} \times 1\frac{1}{2} = \frac{5}{2} \times \frac{3}{2} = \frac{15}{4} = 3\frac{3}{4}$

Multiply.

Rewrite as improper fractions.

Visual Model

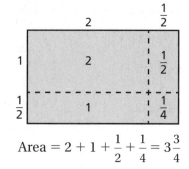

$$Area = 2 + 1 + \frac{1}{2} + \frac{1}{4} = 3\frac{3}{4}$$

Skill Examples

1. $3\frac{1}{2} \times 2\frac{1}{3} = \frac{7}{2} \times \frac{7}{3} = \frac{49}{6} = 8\frac{1}{6}$

2. $1\frac{3}{4} \times 4\frac{1}{2} = \frac{7}{4} \times \frac{9}{2} = \frac{63}{8} = 7\frac{7}{8}$

3. $2\frac{2}{5} \times 1\frac{2}{3} = \frac{12}{5} \times \frac{5}{3} = \frac{60}{15} = 4$

4. $1\frac{1}{2} \times 1\frac{1}{2} = \frac{3}{2} \times \frac{3}{2} = \frac{9}{4} = 2\frac{1}{4}$

Application Example

5. Your friend earns $7\frac{1}{2}$ dollars each hour she works. How much money will she earn after working $4\frac{1}{2}$ hours?

$$7\frac{1}{2} \times 4\frac{1}{2} = \frac{15}{2} \times \frac{9}{2} = \frac{135}{4} = 33\frac{3}{4}$$

She will earn $33\frac{3}{4}$ dollars, or $33.75.

PRACTICE MAKES *PURR*-FECT®

Check your answers at BigIdeasMath.com.

Find the product. Write your answer in simplest form.

6. $2\frac{1}{3} \times 1\frac{1}{3} =$ _____

7. $4\frac{2}{3} \times 1\frac{1}{2} =$ _____

8. $1\frac{1}{2} \times 3 =$ _____

9. $5\frac{1}{6} \times \frac{1}{3} =$ _____

10. $\frac{3}{4} \times 3\frac{1}{2} =$ _____

11. $5 \times 4\frac{1}{2} =$ _____

12. $2\frac{1}{7} \times \frac{7}{15} =$ _____

13. $1\frac{3}{5} \times \frac{3}{8} =$ _____

14. $1\frac{1}{3} \times 1\frac{1}{3} =$ _____

15. $2\frac{2}{3} \times 3\frac{1}{3} =$ _____

16. $2\frac{1}{4} \times 8 =$ _____

17. $3\frac{1}{2} \times \frac{1}{2} \times \frac{1}{2} =$ _____

Find the area of the rectangle.

18.

$\frac{3}{2}$ in.

$2\frac{1}{2}$ in.

Area = _____

19.

$2\frac{2}{3}$ cm

4 cm

Area = _____

20. **RECIPE** Rewrite the recipe so that each ingredient is one-third of the full recipe.

$2\frac{1}{2}$ cups flour

2 tsp baking powder

4 Tbsp butter

$\frac{1}{2}$ tsp salt

$\frac{3}{4}$ cup milk

_____ cup flour   _____ tsp salt

_____ tsp baking powder   _____ cup milk

_____ Tbsp butter

REVIEW: Dividing Mixed Numbers

Name _____

Key Concept and Vocabulary

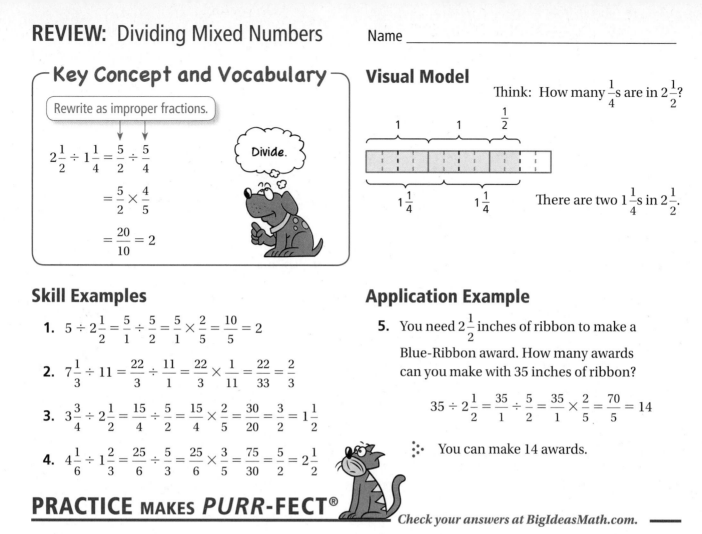

Rewrite as improper fractions.

$$2\frac{1}{2} \div 1\frac{1}{4} = \frac{5}{2} \div \frac{5}{4}$$

Divide.

$$= \frac{5}{2} \times \frac{4}{5}$$

$$= \frac{20}{10} = 2$$

Visual Model

Think: How many $\frac{1}{4}$s are in $2\frac{1}{2}$?

There are two $1\frac{1}{4}$s in $2\frac{1}{2}$.

Skill Examples

1. $5 \div 2\frac{1}{2} = \frac{5}{1} \div \frac{5}{2} = \frac{5}{1} \times \frac{2}{5} = \frac{10}{5} = 2$

2. $7\frac{1}{3} \div 11 = \frac{22}{3} \div \frac{11}{1} = \frac{22}{3} \times \frac{1}{11} = \frac{22}{33} = \frac{2}{3}$

3. $3\frac{3}{4} \div 2\frac{1}{2} = \frac{15}{4} \div \frac{5}{2} = \frac{15}{4} \times \frac{2}{5} = \frac{30}{20} = \frac{3}{2} = 1\frac{1}{2}$

4. $4\frac{1}{6} \div 1\frac{2}{3} = \frac{25}{6} \div \frac{5}{3} = \frac{25}{6} \times \frac{3}{5} = \frac{75}{30} = \frac{5}{2} = 2\frac{1}{2}$

Application Example

5. You need $2\frac{1}{2}$ inches of ribbon to make a Blue-Ribbon award. How many awards can you make with 35 inches of ribbon?

$$35 \div 2\frac{1}{2} = \frac{35}{1} \div \frac{5}{2} = \frac{35}{1} \times \frac{2}{5} = \frac{70}{5} = 14$$

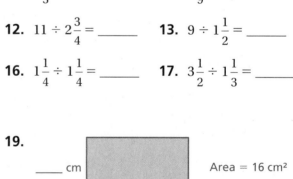

You can make 14 awards.

PRACTICE MAKES *PURR*-FECT®

Check your answers at BigIdeasMath.com.

Find the quotient. Write your answer in simplest form.

6. $4\frac{1}{2} \div 9 =$ _____

7. $3\frac{3}{7} \div 8 =$ _____

8. $4\frac{2}{3} \div 7 =$ _____

9. $1\frac{7}{9} \div 4 =$ _____

10. $8 \div 1\frac{1}{3} =$ _____

11. $32 \div 3\frac{1}{5} =$ _____

12. $11 \div 2\frac{3}{4} =$ _____

13. $9 \div 1\frac{1}{2} =$ _____

14. $5\frac{1}{2} \div \frac{1}{2} =$ _____

15. $\frac{1}{2} \div 1\frac{1}{2} =$ _____

16. $1\frac{1}{4} \div 1\frac{1}{4} =$ _____

17. $3\frac{1}{2} \div 1\frac{1}{3} =$ _____

Find the unknown measure of the rectangle.

18.

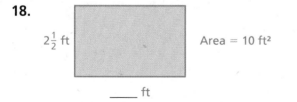

$2\frac{1}{2}$ ft

Area = 10 ft²

_____ ft

19.

_____ cm

Area = 16 cm²

$5\frac{1}{3}$ cm

20. RED RIBBONS You need $3\frac{1}{2}$ inches of ribbon to make a Red-Ribbon award. How many awards can you make with 35 inches of ribbon? _____

21. SHIPPING You are stacking books into a shipping box that is 15 inches high. Each book is $1\frac{1}{4}$ inches thick. How many books can you fit in a stack? _____

REVIEW: Decimal Place Value

Name _____

Key Concept and Vocabulary

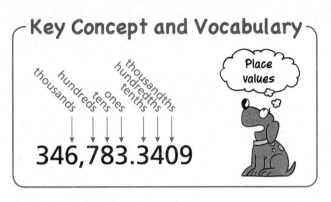

thousands
hundreds
tens
ones
tenths
hundredths
thousandths

Place values

346,783.3409

Visual Model

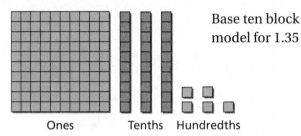

Ones   Tenths   Hundredths

Base ten block model for 1.35

Skill Examples

1. Standard form: 1.4
   Word form: one *and* four tenths

2. Standard form: 2.07
   Word form: two *and* seven hundredths

3. Standard form: 14.009
   Word form: fourteen *and* nine thousandths

Application Example

4. The stopwatch shows a runner's 100-meter dash time. Write the time in words.

14.97 seconds

∴ Fourteen and ninety-seven hundredths seconds

PRACTICE MAKES PURR-FECT®

Check your answers at *BigIdeasMath.com.*

Write the decimal in word form.

5. 182.1 _____

6. 27.35 _____

Write the standard form for the words.

7. Five thousand seven hundred forty-nine *and* one tenth _____

8. Nine hundred eighteen *and* fifty-seven thousandths _____

Write the decimal given by the model.

9.
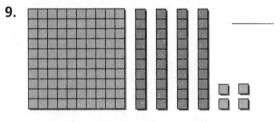
_____

10.
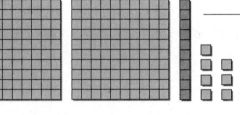
_____

Write the time in words.

11.

8.53 seconds

_____

12.

11.68 seconds

_____

REVIEW: Comparing and Ordering Decimals

Name _____

Key Concept and Vocabulary

is less than → 1.23 < 1.24

is greater than → 1.24 > 1.23

Order decimals.

Visual Model

Number Line

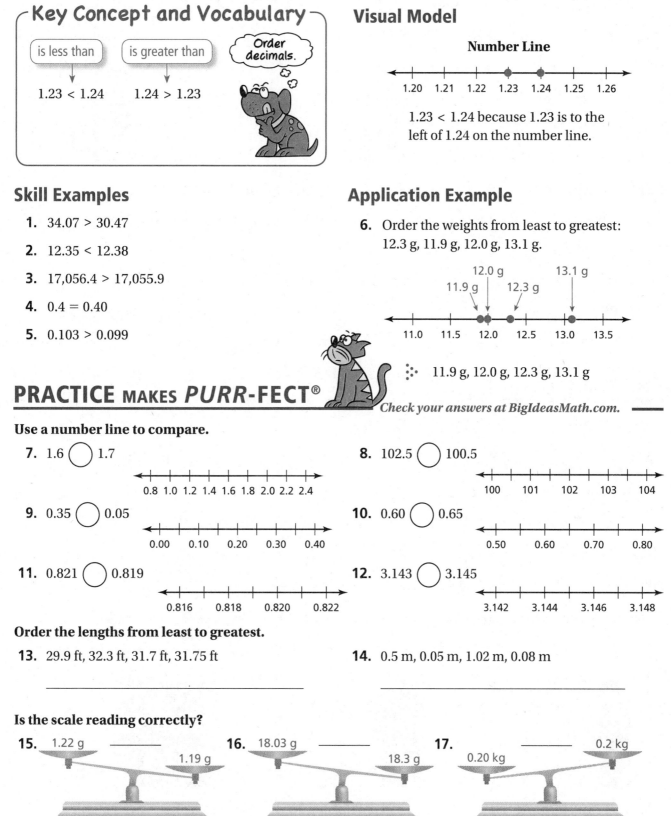

1.20 1.21 1.22 1.23 1.24 1.25 1.26

1.23 < 1.24 because 1.23 is to the left of 1.24 on the number line.

Skill Examples

1. 34.07 > 30.47

2. 12.35 < 12.38

3. 17,056.4 > 17,055.9

4. 0.4 = 0.40

5. 0.103 > 0.099

Application Example

6. Order the weights from least to greatest: 12.3 g, 11.9 g, 12.0 g, 13.1 g.

11.9 g   12.0 g   12.3 g   13.1 g

11.0 11.5 12.0 12.5 13.0 13.5

⋮ 11.9 g, 12.0 g, 12.3 g, 13.1 g

Check your answers at BigIdeasMath.com.

PRACTICE MAKES *PURR*-FECT®

Use a number line to compare.

7. 1.6 ◯ 1.7

0.8 1.0 1.2 1.4 1.6 1.8 2.0 2.2 2.4

8. 102.5 ◯ 100.5

100 101 102 103 104

9. 0.35 ◯ 0.05

0.00 0.10 0.20 0.30 0.40

10. 0.60 ◯ 0.65

0.50 0.60 0.70 0.80

11. 0.821 ◯ 0.819

0.816 0.818 0.820 0.822

12. 3.143 ◯ 3.145

3.142 3.144 3.146 3.148

Order the lengths from least to greatest.

13. 29.9 ft, 32.3 ft, 31.7 ft, 31.75 ft

_____

14. 0.5 m, 0.05 m, 1.02 m, 0.08 m

_____

Is the scale reading correctly?

15. 1.22 g ——— 1.19 g

16. 18.03 g ——— 18.3 g

17. 0.20 kg ——— 0.2 kg

18. **OPEN-ENDED** Newton is thinking of a number that is greater than 0.4 and less than 0.5. The greatest digit in the number is in the hundredths place. What might Newton's number be? _____

Key Concept and Vocabulary

$\frac{1}{10} = 0.1$ $\frac{86}{100} = 0.86$

$1\frac{216}{1,000} = 1.216$ $\frac{25}{100} = \frac{1}{4} = 0.25$

Fractions and decimals

Visual Models

$\frac{2}{10} = 0.2$

$\frac{62}{100} = 0.62$

Skill Examples

1. $\frac{6}{10} = 0.6$

2. $1\frac{73}{100} = 1.73$

3. $3.8 = 3\frac{8}{10}$

4. $0.05 = \frac{5}{100}$

5. $0.875 = \frac{875}{1,000}$

6. $\frac{4}{5} = \frac{4 \cdot 2}{5 \cdot 2} = \frac{8}{10} = 0.8$

Application Example

7. You put 16.75 gallons of gas in your car. Write this decimal as a mixed number.

$$16.75 = 16 + 0.75 = 16\frac{75}{100}$$

⁝⁚ You put $16\frac{75}{100}$ gallons of gas in your car.

PRACTICE MAKES *PURR*-FECT®

Check your answers at BigIdeasMath.com.

Write the fraction or mixed number as a decimal.

8. $\frac{7}{10} =$ _____

9. $4\frac{9}{10} =$ _____

10. $\frac{17}{100} =$ _____

11. $12\frac{31}{100} =$ _____

12. $\frac{109}{1,000} =$ _____

13. $6\frac{48}{1,000} =$ _____

14. $\frac{3}{5} =$ _____

15. $\frac{4}{25} =$ _____

Write the decimal as a fraction or mixed number.

16. $0.4 =$ _____

17. $0.35 =$ _____

18. $1.1 =$ _____

19. $0.095 =$ _____

Write the number represented by the model as a decimal and as a fraction.

20. _____ = _____

21. _____ = _____

22. _____ = _____

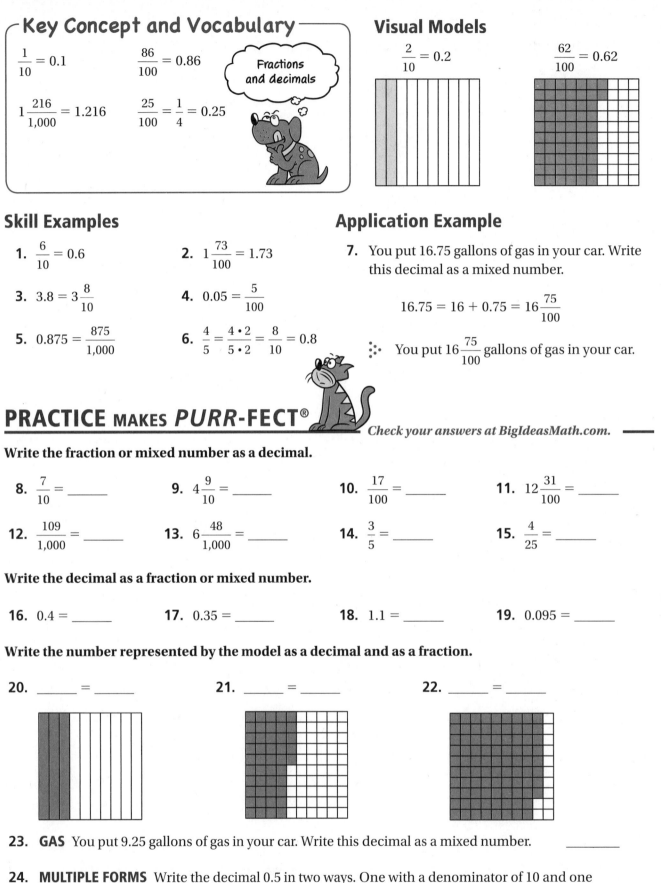

23. **GAS** You put 9.25 gallons of gas in your car. Write this decimal as a mixed number.   _____

24. **MULTIPLE FORMS** Write the decimal 0.5 in two ways. One with a denominator of 10 and one with a denominator of 100.   _____

REVIEW: Rounding Decimals

Name _____

Key Concept and Vocabulary

round up	round down	Rounding

Decision digit is 5, 6, 7, 8, or 9.

Decision digit is 0, 1, 2, 3, or 4.

Visual Model

Round 3.63 to the *nearest tenth*.

3.63

3.6   3.65   3.7

3.63 is closer to 3.6 than to 3.7. So, 3.63 rounds to 3.6.

Skill Examples

1. To the *nearest whole number*:
   3.129 rounds to 3.

2. To the *nearest tenth*:
   4.78 rounds to 4.8.

3. To the *nearest hundredth*:
   0.143 rounds to 0.14.

Application Example

4. The price of 1 gallon of gasoline is $2.899. Round this price to the nearest cent.

   To the *nearest cent*: 2.899 rounds to 2.90.

   The price of 1 gallon of gasoline is about $2.90.

PRACTICE MAKES PURR-FECT®

Check your answers at BigIdeasMath.com.

Round to the nearest whole number.

5. 5.74 _____   6. 1.004 _____   7. 26.237 _____   8. 4.506 _____

Round to the nearest tenth.

9. 0.16 _____   10. 0.738 _____   11. 1.05 _____   12. 10.049 _____

Round to the nearest hundredth.

13. 0.012 _____   14. 2.406 _____   15. 0.463 _____   16. 12.006 _____

Round the butterfly's weight to the nearest hundredth of a gram.

17.   0.034 g

18.   0.107 g

19.   0.008 g

_____   _____   _____

20. **PRICE OF GAS** The price of 1 gallon of gasoline is $2.479. Round this price to the nearest cent. _____

21. **BUTTERFLY WEIGHTS** All species of butterflies weigh between 0.003 gram and 3 grams. Explain why it would *not* make sense to round some butterfly weights to the nearest hundredth of a gram.

_____

_____

REVIEW: Estimating Decimal Sums and Differences

Name _____

Key Concept and Vocabulary

You can use rounding to estimate sums and differences of decimals.

Estimation

$$11.4 \longrightarrow 11$$
$$+\ 12.8 \longrightarrow +\ 13$$
$$\overline{ \quad 24}$$

Visual Model

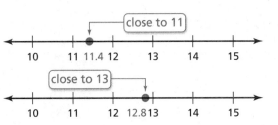
close to 11

10 11 11.4 12 13 14 15

close to 13

10 11 12 12.8 13 14 15

11.4 + 12.8 is about 11 + 13 = 24.

Skill Examples

1. $$4.36 \longrightarrow 4$$
    $$+\ 2.87 \longrightarrow +\ 3$$
    $$\overline{ \quad 7}$$

2. $$9.8 \longrightarrow 10$$
    $$-\ 5.4 \longrightarrow -\ 5$$
    $$\overline{ \quad 5}$$

Application Example

3. Estimate the total length of the cheetah.

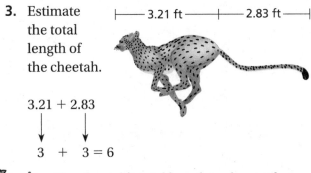
├── 3.21 ft ──┤├── 2.83 ft ──┤

$$3.21 + 2.83$$
$$\downarrow \qquad \downarrow$$
$$3 \ + \ 3 = 6$$

The cheetah's total length is about 6 feet.

PRACTICE MAKES PURR-FECT®

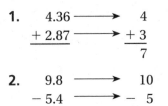

Check your answers at BigIdeasMath.com.

Estimate the sum or difference.

4. 3.6 − 2.7 _____

5. 9.03 − 6.78 _____

6. 2.3 + 5.6 _____

7. 8.21 − 4.11 _____

8. 5.68 + 4.38 _____

9. 3.9 + 3.9 _____

10. 2.61 + 3.45 _____

11. 12.07 − 1.25 _____

12. 10.04 − 6.79 _____

Estimate the total cost of the two shirts.

13.

$17.89 $15.07   **14.** $23.49 $22.99

_____   _____

15. **SHOPPING** At the grocery store, you buy items for $1.79, $3.15, $2.45, $9.08, and $3.99. Estimate the total amount you spend. _____

16. **HAMBURGERS** You buy 2 hamburgers that cost $6.15 each. Estimate the total cost of the hamburgers.

REVIEW: Adding and Subtracting Decimals

Name _____

Key Concept and Vocabulary

$$\begin{array}{r} 5.70 \\ + 3.36 \\ \hline 9.06 \end{array} \qquad \begin{array}{r} 12.72 \\ - 3.84 \\ \hline 8.88 \end{array}$$

Adding and subtracting

Lining up like place values also lines up the decimal points.

Visual Model

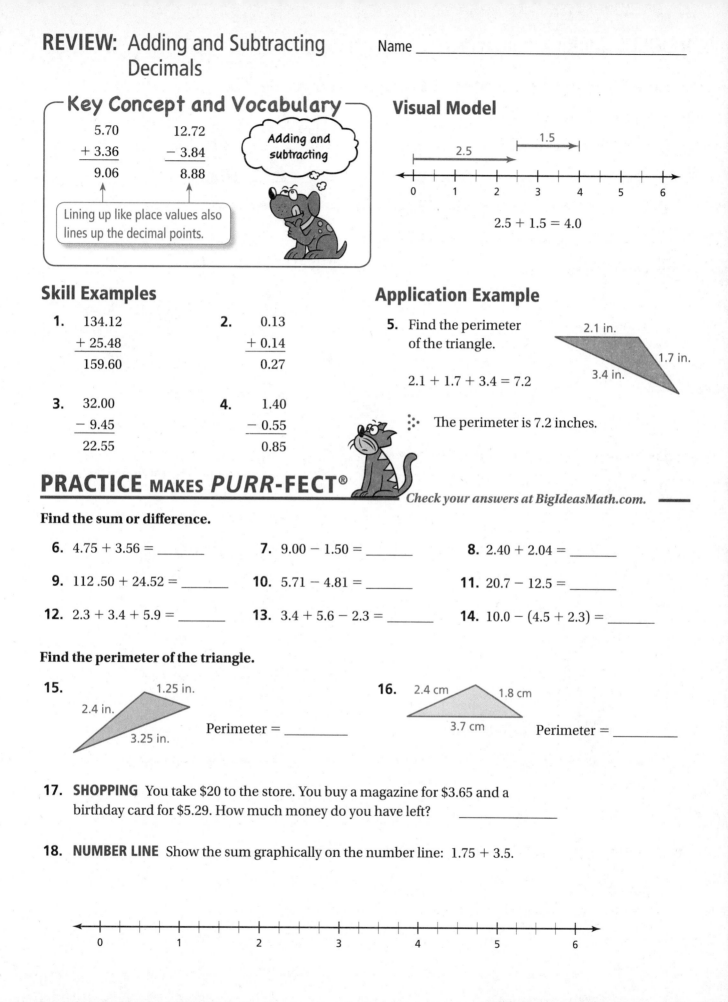

$$2.5 + 1.5 = 4.0$$

Skill Examples

1. $\begin{array}{r} 134.12 \\ + 25.48 \\ \hline 159.60 \end{array}$

2. $\begin{array}{r} 0.13 \\ + 0.14 \\ \hline 0.27 \end{array}$

3. $\begin{array}{r} 32.00 \\ - 9.45 \\ \hline 22.55 \end{array}$

4. $\begin{array}{r} 1.40 \\ - 0.55 \\ \hline 0.85 \end{array}$

Application Example

5. Find the perimeter of the triangle.

   $2.1 + 1.7 + 3.4 = 7.2$

   2.1 in.
   1.7 in.
   3.4 in.

   :: The perimeter is 7.2 inches.

PRACTICE MAKES PURR-FECT®

Check your answers at BigIdeasMath.com.

Find the sum or difference.

6. $4.75 + 3.56 =$ _____

7. $9.00 - 1.50 =$ _____

8. $2.40 + 2.04 =$ _____

9. $112.50 + 24.52 =$ _____

10. $5.71 - 4.81 =$ _____

11. $20.7 - 12.5 =$ _____

12. $2.3 + 3.4 + 5.9 =$ _____

13. $3.4 + 5.6 - 2.3 =$ _____

14. $10.0 - (4.5 + 2.3) =$ _____

Find the perimeter of the triangle.

15.   1.25 in.
      2.4 in.
      3.25 in.

      Perimeter = _____

16.   2.4 cm   1.8 cm
      3.7 cm

      Perimeter = _____

17. **SHOPPING** You take $20 to the store. You buy a magazine for $3.65 and a birthday card for $5.29. How much money do you have left? _____

18. **NUMBER LINE** Show the sum graphically on the number line: $1.75 + 3.5$.

REVIEW: Multiplying Decimals

Name _____

Key Concept and Vocabulary

$$2.15 \leftarrow \text{2 decimal places}$$
$$\times 3.2 \leftarrow \text{+ 1 decimal place}$$
$$430$$
$$\underline{645}$$
$$6.880 \leftarrow \text{3 decimal places}$$

Multiply.

Visual Model

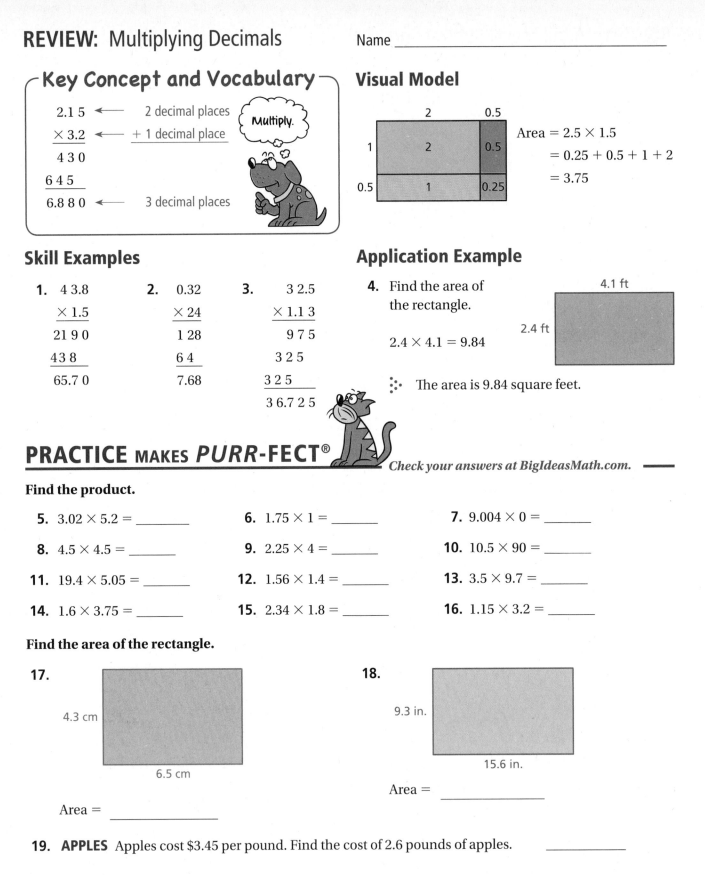

Area $= 2.5 \times 1.5$
$= 0.25 + 0.5 + 1 + 2$
$= 3.75$

Skill Examples

1. 43.8
  $\times 1.5$
  2190
  $\underline{438}$
  65.70

2. 0.32
  $\times 24$
  128
  $\underline{64}$
  7.68

3. 32.5
  $\times 1.13$
  975
  325
  $\underline{325}$
  36.725

Application Example

4. Find the area of the rectangle.

$2.4 \times 4.1 = 9.84$

4.1 ft

2.4 ft

The area is 9.84 square feet.

PRACTICE MAKES *PURR*-FECT®

Check your answers at BigIdeasMath.com.

Find the product.

5. $3.02 \times 5.2 =$ _____

6. $1.75 \times 1 =$ _____

7. $9.004 \times 0 =$ _____

8. $4.5 \times 4.5 =$ _____

9. $2.25 \times 4 =$ _____

10. $10.5 \times 90 =$ _____

11. $19.4 \times 5.05 =$ _____

12. $1.56 \times 1.4 =$ _____

13. $3.5 \times 9.7 =$ _____

14. $1.6 \times 3.75 =$ _____

15. $2.34 \times 1.8 =$ _____

16. $1.15 \times 3.2 =$ _____

Find the area of the rectangle.

17.

4.3 cm

6.5 cm

Area = _____

18.

9.3 in.

15.6 in.

Area = _____

19. APPLES Apples cost $3.45 per pound. Find the cost of 2.6 pounds of apples. _____

20. PEACHES Peaches cost $4.28 per pound. Find the cost of two and a quarter pounds of peaches. Show your work. _____

REVIEW: Dividing Decimals

Name _____

Key Concept and Vocabulary

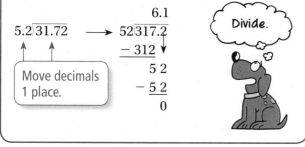

$$5.2\overline{)31.72} \longrightarrow 52\overline{)317.2}$$

$$\begin{array}{r} 6.1 \\ 52\overline{)317.2} \\ -312 \downarrow \\ \hline 5\,2 \\ -5\,2 \\ \hline 0 \end{array}$$

Move decimals 1 place.

Divide.

Visual Model

$$1.5 \div 5 = 0.3$$

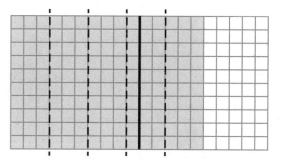

When you divide 1.5 into 5 equal groups, each group will be 0.3.

Skill Examples

1. $65.3 \div 10 = 6.53$

2. $65.3 \div 100 = 0.653$

3. $65.3 \div 1000 = 0.0653$

Each time you divide a number by 10, each digit in the number shifts one position to the right in a place value chart.

Application Example

4. A prize of $104.32 is divided equally among four people. How much does each person get?

$$104.32 \div 4 = 26.08$$

∴ Each person gets $26.08.

PRACTICE MAKES PURR-FECT®

Check your answers at BigIdeasMath.com.

Find the quotient.

5. $5.2 \div 10 =$ _____

6. $73.1 \div 100 =$ _____

7. $1500 \div 1000 =$ _____

8. $0.58 \div 2 =$ _____

9. $19.3 \div 1 =$ _____

10. $19.7 \div 0.1 =$ _____

11. $78.4 \div 1.4 =$ _____

12. $1000 \div 12.5 =$ _____

13. $3.42 \div 0.36 =$ _____

14. $18.98 \div 3.65 =$ _____

15. $4.5 \div 1.25 =$ _____

16. $29.45 \div 4.75 =$ _____

Find the width of the rectangle.

17.

____ cm

Area = 35.36 cm²

6.8 cm

18.

____ in.

15.2 in.

Area = 129.2 in.²

19. **DRIVING TRIP** You drive 1400 miles in 3.5 days. You drive an equal number of miles each day. How many miles do you drive each day? _____

Key Concept and Vocabulary

$$30\% = \frac{30}{100}$$

30 ← 30
per ← per
cent (100) ← cent (100)

Percent

Visual Model

30% is equal to 30 parts out of 100 parts.

Skill Examples

30% of 10 is 3:

1. 30% of 10 is 3: $\frac{30}{100} \cdot 10 = 3$

2. 25% of 8 is 2: $\frac{25}{100} \cdot 8 = 2$

3. 50% of 24 is 12: $\frac{50}{100} \cdot 24 = 12$

4. 75% of 80 is 60: $\frac{75}{100} \cdot 80 = 60$

Application Example

5. You earn $100,000 and have to pay 40% federal income tax. How much in federal income tax do you pay?

$$\frac{40}{100} \cdot 100,000 = 40,000.$$

You pay $40,000 in federal income tax.

PRACTICE MAKES *PURR*-FECT®

Check your answers at BigIdeasMath.com.

Find the percent of the number.

6. 20% of 50 = _____   7. 10% of 80 = _____   8. 1% of 100 = _____   9. 25% of 16 = _____

10. 30% of 40 = _____   11. 100% of 5 = _____   12. 60% of 60 = _____   13. 75% of 40 = _____

14. 25% of 200 = _____   15. 10% of 120 = _____   16. 0% of 10 = _____   17. 50% of 42 = _____

Shade the model to show the given percent.

18. 25%   19. 82%   20. 37%

21. **TEST SCORE** You take a test that has 20 questions and you get 80% of the questions correct. How many questions do you get correct? _____

22. **SALES TAX** You buy $50 worth of clothes. The sales tax is 8%. How much sales tax do you pay? _____

REVIEW: Percents and Fractions

Name _____

Key Concept and Vocabulary

$$35\% = \frac{35}{100} = \frac{\cancel{5} \cdot 7}{\cancel{5} \cdot 20} = \frac{7}{20}$$

Write as a fraction.

Write percent as a fraction in simplest form.

Visual Model

$$35\% = \frac{7}{20}$$

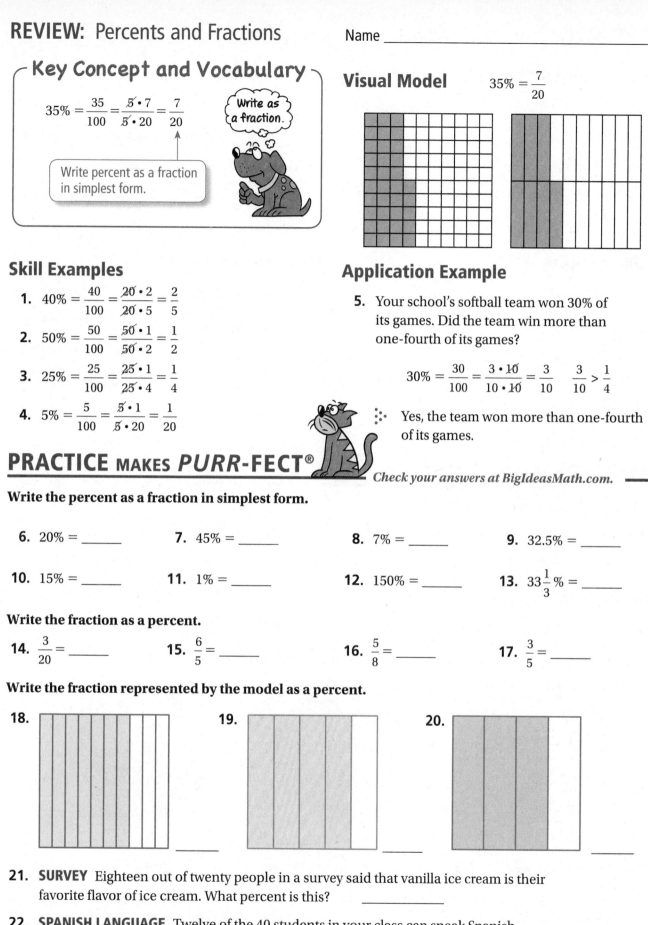

Skill Examples

1. $40\% = \dfrac{40}{100} = \dfrac{\cancel{20} \cdot 2}{\cancel{20} \cdot 5} = \dfrac{2}{5}$

2. $50\% = \dfrac{50}{100} = \dfrac{\cancel{50} \cdot 1}{\cancel{50} \cdot 2} = \dfrac{1}{2}$

3. $25\% = \dfrac{25}{100} = \dfrac{\cancel{25} \cdot 1}{\cancel{25} \cdot 4} = \dfrac{1}{4}$

4. $5\% = \dfrac{5}{100} = \dfrac{\cancel{5} \cdot 1}{\cancel{5} \cdot 20} = \dfrac{1}{20}$

Application Example

5. Your school's softball team won 30% of its games. Did the team win more than one-fourth of its games?

$$30\% = \frac{30}{100} = \frac{3 \cdot \cancel{10}}{10 \cdot \cancel{10}} = \frac{3}{10} \qquad \frac{3}{10} > \frac{1}{4}$$

Yes, the team won more than one-fourth of its games.

PRACTICE MAKES PURR-FECT®

Check your answers at BigIdeasMath.com.

Write the percent as a fraction in simplest form.

6. $20\% = $ _____

7. $45\% = $ _____

8. $7\% = $ _____

9. $32.5\% = $ _____

10. $15\% = $ _____

11. $1\% = $ _____

12. $150\% = $ _____

13. $33\frac{1}{3}\% = $ _____

Write the fraction as a percent.

14. $\dfrac{3}{20} = $ _____

15. $\dfrac{6}{5} = $ _____

16. $\dfrac{5}{8} = $ _____

17. $\dfrac{3}{5} = $ _____

Write the fraction represented by the model as a percent.

18. _____

19. _____

20. _____

21. **SURVEY** Eighteen out of twenty people in a survey said that vanilla ice cream is their favorite flavor of ice cream. What percent is this? _____

22. **SPANISH LANGUAGE** Twelve of the 40 students in your class can speak Spanish. What percent is this? _____

REVIEW: Percents and Decimals

Name _____

Key Concept and Vocabulary

18% = 0.18

Percent to Decimal: Move decimal point to the left 2 places.

0.73 = 73%

Decimal to Percent: Move decimal point to the right 2 places.

Write as decimal.

Visual Model

18% = 0.18

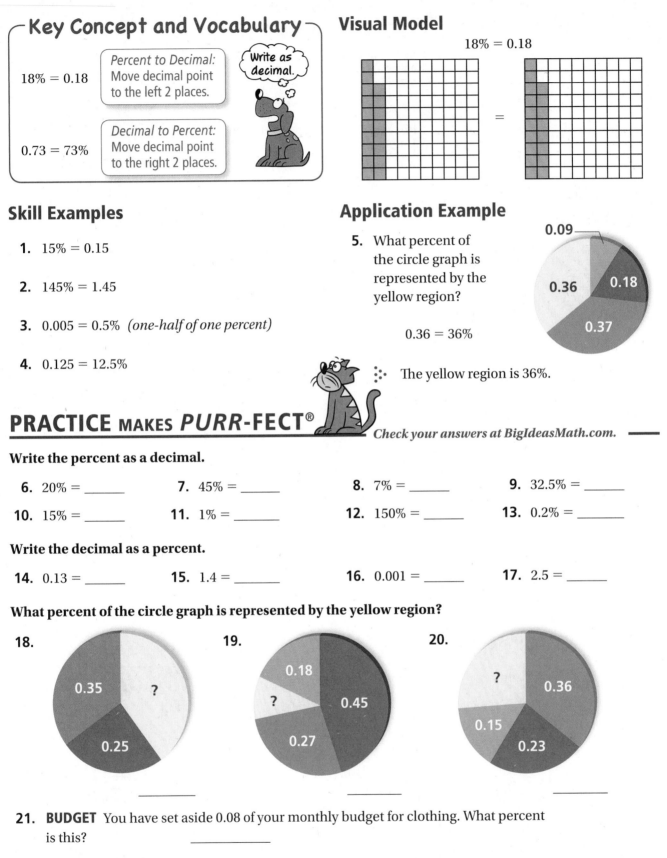

Skill Examples

1. 15% = 0.15

2. 145% = 1.45

3. 0.005 = 0.5% *(one-half of one percent)*

4. 0.125 = 12.5%

Application Example

5. What percent of the circle graph is represented by the yellow region?

0.36 = 36%

The yellow region is 36%.

0.09
0.18
0.36
0.37

PRACTICE MAKES PURR-FECT®

Check your answers at BigIdeasMath.com.

Write the percent as a decimal.

6. 20% = _____   7. 45% = _____   8. 7% = _____   9. 32.5% = _____

10. 15% = _____   11. 1% = _____   12. 150% = _____ 13. 0.2% = _____

Write the decimal as a percent.

14. 0.13 = _____ 15. 1.4 = _____   16. 0.001 = _____ 17. 2.5 = _____

What percent of the circle graph is represented by the yellow region?

18.

0.35   ?
0.25

_____

19.

0.18
?   0.45
0.27

_____

20.

?   0.36
0.15
0.23

_____

21. **BUDGET** You have set aside 0.08 of your monthly budget for clothing. What percent is this? _____

22. **SUMMER SCHOOL** Eighty-seven percent of the students in your class do not plan to attend summer school. What percent of your class plans to attend summer school? _____

REVIEW: Comparing Percents

Name _____

Key Concept and Vocabulary

is less than   is greater than

16% < 28%   28% > 16%

inequality signs

Comparing percents

Visual Model

16%   <   28%

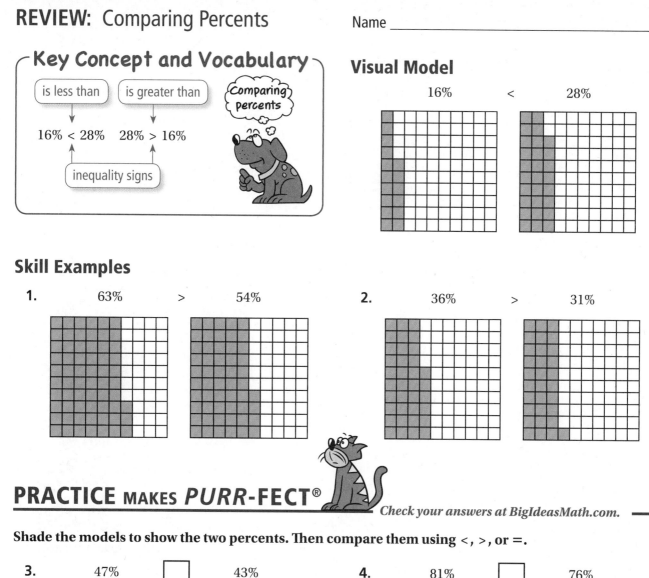

Skill Examples

1.   63%   >   54%

2.   36%   >   31%

PRACTICE MAKES *PURR*-FECT®

Check your answers at BigIdeasMath.com.

Shade the models to show the two percents. Then compare them using <, >, or =.

3.   47%   ☐   43%

4.   81%   ☐   76%

Classroom A   Classroom B

5. **FUNDRAISER** Two classrooms are having a fundraiser. After one week, Classroom A has raised 26% of its goal and Classroom B has raised 29% of its goal. Shade the models to show the two percents. Which classroom has raised a greater percentage of its goal?

_____

REVIEW: The Percent Proportion

Name _____

Key Concept and Vocabulary

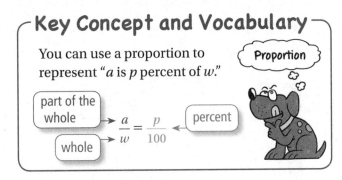

You can use a proportion to represent "a is p percent of w."

part of the whole → $\dfrac{a}{w} = \dfrac{p}{100}$ ← percent

whole →

Proportion

Visual Model

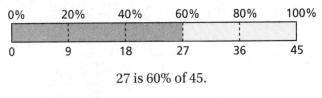

0%	20%	40%	60%	80%	100%
0	9	18	27	36	45

27 is 60% of 45.

Skill Examples

1. $\dfrac{36}{50} = \dfrac{p}{100}$

$100 \cdot \dfrac{36}{50} = 100 \cdot \dfrac{p}{100}$

$72 = p$

⋰• So, 36 is 72% of 50.

2. $\dfrac{a}{36} = \dfrac{20}{100}$

$36 \cdot \dfrac{a}{36} = 36 \cdot \dfrac{20}{100}$

$a = 7.2$

⋰• So, 7.2 is 20% of 36.

Application Example

3. A basketball player makes 45%, or 9 shots, of her attempted shots. How many shots did the basketball player attempt?

$\dfrac{9}{w} = \dfrac{45}{100}$

$9 \cdot 100 = w \cdot 45$

$900 = 45w$

$\dfrac{900}{45} = \dfrac{45w}{45}$

$20 = w$

⋰• The basketball player attempted 20 shots.

PRACTICE MAKES PURR-FECT®

Check your answers at BigIdeasMath.com. ──

Write and solve a proportion to answer the question.

4. 68 is what percent of 80?

_____

5. What number is 25% of 116?

_____

6. 36 is 16% of what number?

_____

7. 48 is what percent of 128?

_____

8. What number is 64% of 40?

_____

9. 77 is 55% of what number?

_____

10. **PLAY** Students are auditioning for a play. Of the 60 students auditioning, 12 will get a part in the play. What percent of the students who audition will get a part in the play?

_____

11. **HOMEWORK** You have completed 60% of your English homework. The assignment has 25 questions. How many questions are left? _____

REVIEW: The Percent Equation

Name _____

Key Concept and Vocabulary

You can use an equation to represent "*a* is *p* percent of *w*."

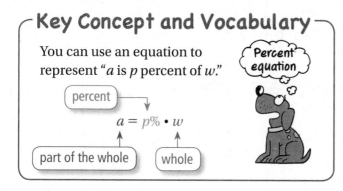

percent

$$a = p\% \cdot w$$

part of the whole   whole

Visual Model

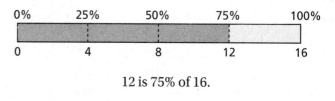

0%	25%	50%	75%	100%
0	4	8	12	16

12 is 75% of 16.

Skill Examples

1. 12 is what percent of 80?

$$12 = p\% \cdot 80$$

$$\frac{12}{80} = \frac{p\% \cdot 80}{80}$$

$$0.15 = p\%$$

∴ So, 12 is 15% of 80.

2. What number is 45% of 40?

$$a = \frac{45}{100} \cdot 40$$

$$a = 18$$

∴ So, 18 is 45% of 40.

Application Example

3. You earn 34 points on a test, which is 85% of the total points. How many points is the test worth?

$$34 = 0.85 \cdot w$$

$$\frac{34}{0.85} = \frac{0.85 \cdot w}{0.85}$$

$$40 = w$$

∴ The test is worth 40 points.

PRACTICE MAKES *PURR-FECT*®

Check your answers at BigIdeasMath.com.

Write and solve an equation to answer the question.

4. 18 is what percent of 90?

_____

5. 66 is what percent of 120?

_____

6. What number is 42% of 50?

_____

7. 34 is 40% of what number?

_____

8. 180 is 75% of what number?

_____

9. 55 is what percent of 125?

_____

10. **BASEBALL** Of the 25 players on a baseball team, 12 are pitchers. What percent of the players are pitchers?

_____

11. **SURVEY** Students are asked whether they prefer math or science. Of the 120 students surveyed, 65% prefer math. How many of the students prefer science? _____

REVIEW: Estimating and Finding a Discount

Key Concept and Vocabulary

A discount is a decrease in the original price of an item. To find the discount, write the percent as a decimal or fraction and multiply it by the original price of the item.

Discount

Visual Model

0%	20%	40%	60%	80%	100%

| 0 | 15 | 30 | 45 | 60 | 75 |

The sale price of a $75 necklace with a 60% discount is $75 − $45 = $30.

Application Examples

1. The original price of a book is $18.79. The discount is 20%.

   Estimate: Round 18.79 to 20.
   $$0.2 \times 20 = 4$$
   ⋮• The estimate for the discount is $4.

   Actual: $0.2 \times 18.79 \approx 3.76$
   ⋮• The actual discount is $3.76. The sale price of the book is $18.79 − $3.76 = $15.03.

2. The original price of a pair of in-line skates is $209.99. The discount is 15%.

   Estimate: Round 209.99 to 200.
   $$0.15 \times 200 = 30$$
   ⋮• The estimate for the discount is $30.

   Actual: $0.15 \times 209.99 \approx 31.50$
   ⋮• The actual discount is $31.50. The sale price of the pair of in-line skates is $209.99 − $31.50 = $178.49.

PRACTICE MAKES PURR-FECT®

Check your answers at BigIdeasMath.com. ▬

Estimate the discount. Then find the actual discount and the sale price.

3. **TRUMPET** The original price of a trumpet is $319.29. The discount is 25%.

   _____

4. **SHOES** The original price of a pair of shoes is $47.99. The discount is 40%.

   _____

5. **LAMP** The original price of a lamp is $17.09. The discount is 15%.

   _____

6. **RING** The original price of a ring is $96.75. The discount is 60%.

   _____

7. **ELECTRONICS** The original price of a home theater system is $243.89. The discount is 75%.

   _____

8. **BASEBALL** The original price of a baseball glove is $26.99. The discount is 30%.

   _____

9. **SEWING MACHINE** The original price of a sewing machine is $182.96. The discount is 20%.

   _____

REVIEW: Estimating and Finding a Sales Tax

Name _____

Key Concept and Vocabulary

To find the sales tax on an item, write the percent as a decimal or fraction and multiply it by the price of the item.

Sales tax

Visual Model

5%						
0%	20%	40%	60%	80%	100%

0 2.5 5 7.5 10 12.5 15 17.5 20 22.5 25
  1.25

Using a sales tax of 5%, the sales tax on a $25 shirt is $1.25.

Application Examples

1. A DVD costs $20 before tax. The sales tax is 7%.

   Estimate: Round 7% to 5%.

   $$0.05 \times 20 = 1$$

   ∴ The estimate for the sales tax is $1.

   Actual: $0.07 \times 20 = 1.4$

   ∴ The actual sales tax is $1.40.

2. A bicycle costs $115 before tax. The sales tax is 9%.

   Estimate: Round 9% to 10% and 115 to 120.

   $$0.1 \times 120 = 12$$

   ∴ The estimate for the sales tax is $12.

   Actual: $0.09 \times 115 = 10.35$

   ∴ The actual sales tax is $10.35.

PRACTICE MAKES *PURR*-FECT®

Check your answers at BigIdeasMath.com. ▬

Estimate the sales tax. Then find the actual sales tax.

3. **BASEBALL CARDS** The pack of baseball cards costs $3.75 before tax. The sales tax is 4%.

   _____

4. **TELEVISION** A television costs $400 before tax. The sales tax is 8%.

   _____

5. **MP3 PLAYER** An MP3 player costs $89 before tax. The sales tax is 6%.

   _____

6. **COUCH** A couch costs $675 before tax. The sales tax is 5%.

   _____

7. **GUITAR** A guitar costs $299 before tax. The sales tax is 9%.

   _____

8. **TABLE** A table costs $50 before tax. The sales tax is 4.5%.

   _____

9. **JEANS** A pair of jeans costs $39 before tax. The sales tax is 5.5%.

   _____

REVIEW: Estimating and Finding a Tip

Name _____

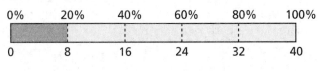

Key Concept and Vocabulary

To find the tip on a food bill at a restaurant, write the percent as a decimal or fraction and multiply it by the cost of the food bill.

Tip

Visual Model

0%	20%	40%	60%	80%	100%

| 0 | 8 | 16 | 24 | 32 | 40 |

A 20% tip on a food bill of $40 is $8.

Application Examples

1. Your food bill at a restaurant is $8.49. You leave a 15% tip.

Estimate: Round 8.49 to 10.

$$0.15 \times 10 = 1.5$$

⋮· The estimate for the tip is $1.50.

Actual: $0.15 \cdot 8.49 \approx 1.27$

⋮· The actual tip is $1.27.

2. Your food bill at a restaurant is $15.83. You leave a 20% tip.

Estimate: Round 15.83 to 16.

$$0.2 \times 16 = 3.2$$

⋮· The estimate for the tip is $3.20.

Actual: $0.2 \times 15.83 \approx 3.17$

⋮· The actual tip is $3.17.

PRACTICE MAKES *PURR-FECT*®

Check your answers at BigIdeasMath.com. ──

Estimate the tip. Then find the actual tip.

3. Food bill: $33.65; Tip: 15% _____

4. Food bill: $44.28; Tip: 20% _____

5. Food bill: $11.17; Tip: 15% _____

6. Food bill: $12.37; Tip: 20% _____

7. Food bill: $23.16; Tip: 15% _____

8. Food bill: $16.21; Tip: 20% _____

9. Food bill: $37.54; Tip: 25% _____

10. Food bill: $25.96; Tip: 20% _____

11. Food bill: $28.93; Tip: 15% _____

12. Food bill: $72.79; Tip: 25% _____

13. Food bill: $19.82; Tip: 23% _____

14. Food bill: $51.56; Tip: 30% _____

REVIEW: Simple Interest

Name _____

Key Concept and Vocabulary

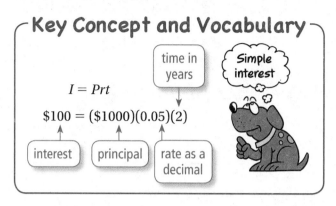

time in years

Simple interest

$I = Prt$

$\$100 = (\$1000)(0.05)(2)$

interest | principal | rate as a decimal

Visual Model

1 month	3 months	4 months
$t = \dfrac{1}{12}$	$t = \dfrac{1}{4}$	$t = \dfrac{1}{3}$

6 months	1 year	2 years
$t = \dfrac{1}{2}$	$t = 1$	$t = 2$

Skill Examples

1. $P = \$200$, $r = 0.10$, $t = 4$ years
   $I = 200(0.10)(4) = \$80$

2. $P = \$250$, $r = 0.04$, $t = 0.5$ year
   $I = 250(0.04)(0.5) = \$5$

3. $P = \$2000$, $r = 0.05$, $t = 20$ years
   $I = 2000(0.05)(20) = \$2000$

Application Example

4. You deposited $500 in a savings account for 10 years. The account paid 6% simple interest. How much interest did you earn?

   $P = \$500$, $r = 0.06$, $t = 10$ years
   $I = 500(0.06)(10) = \$300$

   ∴ You earned $300 in interest.

PRACTICE MAKES PURR-FECT®

Check your answers at BigIdeasMath.com.

Find the simple interest.

5. Principal: $400, Rate: 5%, Time: 3 years

   _____

6. Principal: $100, Rate: 3%, Time: 6 months

   _____

7. Principal: $1000, Rate: 2%, Time: 4 months

   _____

8. Principal: $250, Rate: 10%, Time: 6 months

   _____

9. Principal: $500, Rate: 8%, Time: 9 months

   _____

10. Principal: $600, Rate: 1%, Time: 8 years

    _____

In which savings account do you earn more simple interest?

11. **a.** Deposit $200 at 6% for 3 years.
    b. Deposit $200 at 8% for 18 months.

    _____

12. **a.** Deposit $1000 at 4% for 5 years.
    b. Deposit $1000 at 5% for 4 years.

    _____

13. **SAVINGS** You deposited $600 in a savings account for 5 years. The account paid 4% simple interest. How much interest did you earn? _____

14. **LOAN** You borrowed $1000 for 2 years. You are charged 5% simple interest. How much interest do you owe? _____

REVIEW: Ratios

Name _____

Key Concept and Vocabulary

A **ratio** is a comparison of two quantities.

    3 red buttons to 2 blue buttons

    3 red buttons : 2 blue buttons

The **value of the ratio** of red buttons to blue buttons is $\frac{3}{2}$.

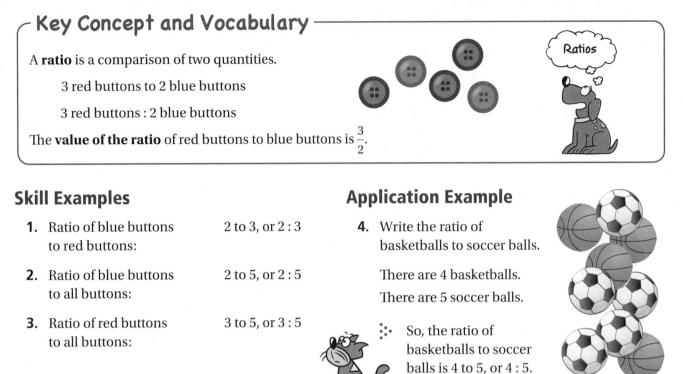

Skill Examples

1. Ratio of blue buttons to red buttons: 2 to 3, or 2 : 3

2. Ratio of blue buttons to all buttons: 2 to 5, or 2 : 5

3. Ratio of red buttons to all buttons: 3 to 5, or 3 : 5

Application Example

4. Write the ratio of basketballs to soccer balls.

   There are 4 basketballs.
   There are 5 soccer balls.

   ⋮ So, the ratio of basketballs to soccer balls is 4 to 5, or 4 : 5.

PRACTICE MAKES *PURR-FECT*®

Check your answers at BigIdeasMath.com.

Write the ratio of green objects to blue objects. Then find the value of the ratio.

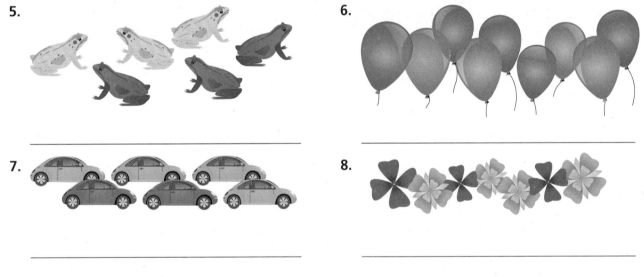

5. _____

6. _____

7. _____

8. _____

Write the ratio of blue objects to *all* objects. Then find the value of the ratio.

9. Frogs in Exercise 5

_____

10. Balloons in Exercise 6

_____

11. Cars in Exercise 7

_____

12. Flowers in Exercise 8

_____

13. **CLASS RATIO** The ratio of boys to girls in a class is 5 to 4. There are 12 girls in the class. How many boys are in the class? _____

REVIEW: Rates

Name _____

Key Concept and Vocabulary

A **rate** is a ratio of two quantities using different units.

You pay $12 for 4 hot dogs.

Rate = $12 : 4 hot dogs

Unit Rate = $3 : 1 hot dog

Visual Model

Rate:

$12 : 4 hot dogs

Unit rate:
$3 : 1 hot dog

Skill Examples

1. You drive 100 miles in 2 hours.
   Your unit rate is 50 miles per hour.

2. You earn $40 in 5 hours.
   Your unit rate is $8 per hour.

3. You save $240 in 6 months.
   Your unit rate is $40 per month.

Application Example

4. Janice grew 8 inches in 4 years. What was her unit rate?

$\div 4$

Inches	8	2
Years	4	1

$\div 4$

∴ Her unit rate is 2 inches per year.

PRACTICE MAKES PURR-FECT®

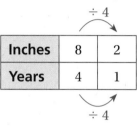

Check your answers at BigIdeasMath.com.

Write a rate for the situation. Then find the unit rate.

5. You fly 2000 miles in 4 hours.

_____ _____
Rate   Unit Rate

6. You pay $15 for 3 pizzas.

_____ _____
Rate   Unit Rate

7. You pay $4 sales tax on 5 identical items.

_____ _____
Rate   Unit Rate

8. You earn $50 for mowing 5 lawns.

_____ _____
Rate   Unit Rate

Decide whether the rates are equivalent.

9. Maria saves $50 in 4 months.
   Ralph saves $60 in 5 months

   _____

10. John rides his bicycle 36 miles in 3 hours.
    Randy rides his bicycle 30 miles in 2.5 hours.

    _____

11. Kim earns $400 for working 40 hours.
    Sam earns $540 for working 45 hours.

    _____

12. Arlene scores 450 points on 5 tests.
    Jolene scores 180 points on 2 tests.

    _____

Name _____

Key Concept and Vocabulary

You can find and organize equivalent ratios in a **ratio table**.
You can find equivalent ratios by:

- adding or subtracting quantities in equivalent ratios.

- multiplying or dividing each quantity in a ratio by the same number.

$+2 \quad +4 \quad \times 3$

Blue Buttons	2	4	8	24
Red Buttons	3	6	12	36

$+3 \quad +6 \quad \times 3$

Ratio tables

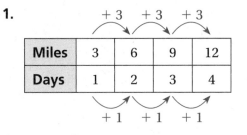

Skill Example

1.

$+3 \quad +3 \quad +3$

Miles	3	6	9	12
Days	1	2	3	4

$+1 \quad +1 \quad +1$

The equivalent ratios are
$3:1, 6:2, 9:3,$ and $12:4.$

Application Example

2. You use 40 tablespoons of flour. How many tablespoons of olive oil do you use?

$\div 2 \quad \times 5$

Olive Oil (tablespoons)	2	1	5
Flour (tablespoons)	16	8	40

$\div 2 \quad \times 5$

⋮⋮ You use 5 tablespoons of olive oil.

PRACTICE MAKES *PURR*-FECT®

Check your answers at BigIdeasMath.com.

Find the missing values in the ratio table.

3.

Feet	42	84		
Seconds	1		3	4

4.

Teachers	2			6
Students	7	14	42	

5.

Bricks	5		4	
Weight (pounds)	35	7		63

6.

Fiber (milligrams)	10	100		15
Servings	2		18	

7. **FUNDRAISER** For every 8 candles that you sell, you raise $96. You raise $288. How many candles did you sell? _____

8. **RUNNING** You run 10 miles in 12 days. Your goal is to run a total of 25 miles in 30 days. Are you on track to meet your goal? Explain.

_____

_____

REVIEW: Proportions

Name _____

Key Concept and Vocabulary

A **proportion** is an equation stating that the values of two ratios are equivalent.

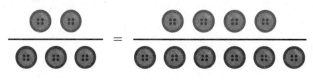

$$\frac{2}{3} = \frac{4}{6}$$ Cross products are equal.

$2 \cdot 6 = 3 \cdot 4$

Visual Model

The value of the ratio "2 to 3" is equal to the value of the ratio "4 to 6."

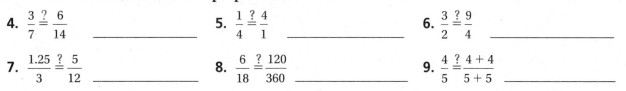

Skill Examples

1. $3 : 5$ and $12 : 20$

   $\frac{3}{5} = \frac{12}{20}$

   The ratios form a proportion because the values of the ratios are equivalent.

2. $1 : 7$ and $7 : 48$

   $\frac{1}{7} \neq \frac{7}{48}$

   The ratios do *not* form a proportion because the values of the ratios are *not* equivalent.

Application Example

3. You spend $5 for 3 tennis balls. Your friend spends $6.25 for 4 tennis balls. Are the two rates proportional?

   $\frac{5}{3} \overset{?}{=} \frac{6.25}{4}$ $5(4) \neq 3(6.25)$

   ∴ The rates are *not* proprotional.

PRACTICE MAKES *PURR*-FECT®

Check your answers at BigIdeasMath.com.

Decide whether the statement is a proportion.

4. $\frac{3}{7} \overset{?}{=} \frac{6}{14}$ _____

5. $\frac{1}{4} \overset{?}{=} \frac{4}{1}$ _____

6. $\frac{3}{2} \overset{?}{=} \frac{9}{4}$ _____

7. $\frac{1.25}{3} \overset{?}{=} \frac{5}{12}$ _____

8. $\frac{6}{18} \overset{?}{=} \frac{120}{360}$ _____

9. $\frac{4}{5} \overset{?}{=} \frac{4+4}{5+5}$ _____

Complete the proportion.

10. $\frac{2}{5} = \frac{\square}{10}$

11. $\frac{1}{6} = \frac{4}{\square}$

12. $\frac{3}{\square} = \frac{9}{24}$

Write the proportion that compares the perimeters to the side lengths of the two squares.

13.

    2   5

    _____

14.

    3   4

    _____

15. **COMPARING RATES** You spend $20 for 5 T-shirts. Your friend spends $15 for 3 T-shirts. Are the two rates proportional? _____

Key Concept and Vocabulary

Operation	Words	Algebra
Addition	the *sum* of	$a + b$
Subtraction	the *difference* of	$a - b$
Multiplication	the *product* of	$a \times b$ $a \cdot b$
Division	the *quotient* of	$a \div b$ $\dfrac{a}{b}$ $b\overline{\smash{)}a}$

The four basic operations are addition, subtraction, multiplication, and division.

Writing expressions

Application Examples

1. A restaurant orders six gallons of orange juice each week. Each gallon contains four quarts. Write an expression to find the total number of quarts of orange juice the restaurant orders each week.

   You want to find the total number of quarts in six groups of four quarts. The phrase *six groups of four* indicates you need to find a product.

   ∴ An expression is 6×4.

2. A 20-fluid-ounce sports drink contains 240 calories. Write an expression to find the number of calories in each fluid ounce.

   You want to find the number of calories per fluid ounce. The phrase *calories per fluid ounce* indicates you need to find the quotient.

   ∴ An expression is $240 \div 20$.

PRACTICE MAKES PURR-FECT®

Check your answers at BigIdeasMath.com.

3. **TEST** The score from your first math test is 82. The score from your second math test is 95. Write an expression to find the increase from the first test to the second test. _____

4. **LAWN** Each weekend, you earn $40 doing lawn work for your neighbor. Write an expression to find how much money you will earn in 6 weeks. _____

5. **FOOD DRIVE** You donate 12 cans of food and 4 boxes of macaroni to a food drive. Write an expression to find the total number of items you donate. _____

6. **BOWLING** You are taking reservations for a bowling party with 35 guests. Each bowling lane can hold 5 bowlers. Write an expression to find the number of lanes the party will need. _____

7. **SHOPPING** You plan to buy a shirt for $24 and a hat for $18. You have $57. Write an expression to find how much money you will have left over. _____

REVIEW: Evaluating Algebraic Expressions

Name _____

Key Concept and Vocabulary

variable

Evaluating expressions

Expression: $2x^2 + 3x - 6$

Evaluate when $x = 2$.

$2(2^2) + 3(2) - 6 = 8 + 6 - 6$
$= 8$

Visual Model

x	$2x + 3$	Value of Expression
1	$2(1) + 3$	5
2	$2(2) + 3$	7
3	$2(3) + 3$	9
4	$2(4) + 3$	11

Skill Examples

1. When $x = 5$, $3x + 4$ is $3(5) + 4 = 19$.

2. When $x = -1$, $5x + 7$ is $5(-1) + 7 = 2$.

3. When $x = 3$, $4x^2$ is $4(3^2) = 36$.

4. When $x = 4$, $x^3 + 1$ is $4^3 + 1 = 65$.

Application Example

5. For a Celsius temperature C, the Fahrenheit temperature F is $\frac{9}{5}C + 32$. Find F when $C = 25°$.

$$\frac{9}{5}C + 32 = \frac{9}{5}(25) + 32$$
$$= 45 + 32$$
$$= 77$$

⋮⋅ The Fahrenheit temperature is $77°$.

Check your answers at BigIdeasMath.com.

PRACTICE MAKES *PURR-FECT*®

Evaluate the expression.

6. When $x = 2$, $3x - 1 =$ _____.

7. When $x = -1$, $3x + 9 =$ _____.

8. When $x = 4$, $x^2 - 5 =$ _____.

9. When $x = \frac{1}{2}$, $3x^2 =$ _____.

10. When $x = 3.1$, $5x + 0.5 =$ _____.

11. When $x = 0$, $4x^2 + 5 =$ _____.

12. When $x = 10$, $x^2 - 8x + 11 =$ _____.

13. When $x = 2\frac{1}{2}$, $6x + 3 =$ _____.

Evaluate the perimeter when $x = 3$.

14. $P =$ _____

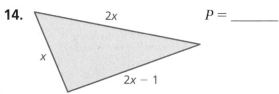

15. $P =$ _____

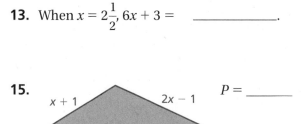

16. **CARDINAL** The weight of the cardinal (in ounces) is $0.6x + 11$ after its eats x ounces of bird seed. How much does it weigh after it eats 2 ounces of bird seed? _____

REVIEW: Writing Algebraic Expressions and Equations

Name _____

Key Concept and Vocabulary

Phrase: Two more than a number

Expression: $2 + n$

_____

Sentence: Two more than a number is equal to six.

Equation: $2 + n = 6$

Visual Model

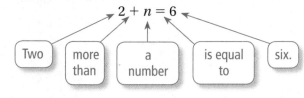

$$2 + n = 6$$

| Two | more than | a number | is equal to | six. |

Skill Examples

1. Five times a number: $5n$

2. Six less than three times a number: $3n - 6$

3. The sum of a number and one: $n + 1$

4. A number divided by three: $n \div 3$

Application Example

5. Write an equation for the following.
   "The price of $15 is the wholesale cost plus a markup of fifty percent."

   Let C be the wholesale cost.

   50% of C is $0.5C$.

   ⋮ An equation is $15 = C + 0.5C$.

PRACTICE MAKES *PURR*-FECT®

Check your answers at BigIdeasMath.com.

Write the verbal phrase as an algebraic expression.

6. The product of a number and two

   _____

7. 10 subtracted from a number

   _____

8. 19 less than twice a number

   _____

9. The sum of a number and three, divided by four

   _____

10. Five times the sum of a number and two

    _____

11. Seven less than four times a number

    _____

Write the sentence as an equation.

12. Three times a number equals nine.

    _____

13. The difference of a number and nine is four.

    _____

14. Twelve divided by a number is four.

    _____

15. The sum of a number and seven is eighteen.

    _____

16. The volume of a cone is one-third the area of the base times the height. A cone has a volume of 20π cubic inches. Write an equation that can be used to solve for the height of the cone.

    _____

h

$B = 4\pi$ in.²

REVIEW: Simplifying Algebraic Expressions

Name _____

Key Concept and Vocabulary

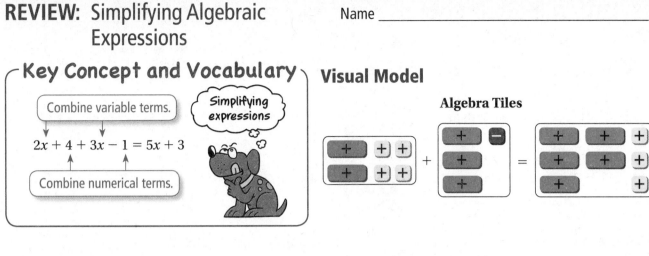

Combine variable terms.

$2x + 4 + 3x - 1 = 5x + 3$

Combine numerical terms.

Simplifying expressions

Visual Model

Algebra Tiles

Skill Examples

1. $2x + 5x = 7x$

2. $1 + n + 4 = n + 5$

3. $(2x + 3) - (x + 2) = x + 1$

4. $2(y - 1) + 3(y + 2) = 5y + 4$

Application Example

5. The original cost of a shirt is x dollars. The shirt is on sale for 30% off. Write a simplified expression for the sale price.

$$x - 0.3x = 0.7x$$

⋮ The sale price is $0.7x$.

PRACTICE MAKES *PURR-FECT*®

Check your answers at BigIdeasMath.com.

Simplify the expression. (*Remove parentheses and combine like terms.*)

6. $4x + 6x =$ _____

7. $3n + 5 - 2n =$ _____

8. $9x + 3 - 6x - 2 =$ _____

9. $3(x + 2) =$ _____

10. $7m - 2m + 5m =$ _____

11. $2 - (x + 1) =$ _____

12. $3x + 6 - x =$ _____

13. $5 - (1 - n) =$ _____

14. $(x + 6) - (x + 6) =$ _____

15. $(4x - 2) + 3(x + 1) =$ _____

16. $(5x + 4) - 2(x + 1) =$ _____

17. $5(x + 2) - 2(x + 2) =$ _____

Write a simplified expression for the perimeter of the rectangle or triangle.

18.

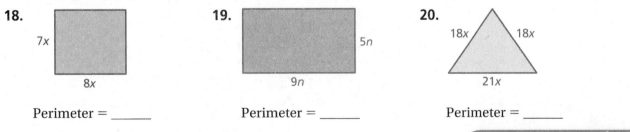

$7x$

$8x$

Perimeter = _____

19.

$5n$

$9n$

Perimeter = _____

20.

$18x$ $18x$

$21x$

Perimeter = _____

21. The original cost of a cell phone is x dollars. The phone is on sale for 35% off. Write a simplified expression for the sale cost. _____

REVIEW: Writing and Graphing Inequalities

Name _____

Key Concept and Vocabulary

$x > 2$: All numbers greater than 2

$x \geq 2$: All numbers greater than or equal to 2

$x < 2$: All numbers less than 2

$x \leq 2$: All numbers less than or equal to 2

Visual Models

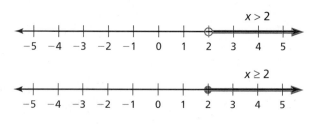

Skill Examples

1. $x > 0$: All positive numbers

2. $x \geq 0$: All nonnegative numbers

3. $x < 0$: All negative numbers

4. $x \leq 0$: All nonpositive numbers

Application Example

5. A sign at a clothing store reads "Savings up to 70%." Let S represent the percent of savings. Write an inequality to describe S.

    S can be equal to 70%.

    Or S can be less than 70%.

    ∵ An inequality is $S \leq 70\%$.

PRACTICE MAKES PURR-FECT®

Check your answers at BigIdeasMath.com.

Write an inequality that represents the numbers described.

6. All numbers that are less than 24

    _____

7. All numbers that are at most 3

    _____

8. All numbers that are greater than 10

    _____

9. All numbers that are no more than 5

    _____

10. All numbers that are at least 11

    _____

11. All numbers that are greater than or equal to 8

    _____

Graph the inequality.

12. $x > -1$

13. $x < 4$

14. $x \leq 3$

15. $x \geq 0$

16. A sign at a shoe store reads "Savings up to 60%." Let P represent the percent of savings. Write an inequality to describe P.

    _____

    Shoe Sale
    Savings
    up to 60%

REVIEW: Properties of Addition and Multiplication

Name _____

Key Concept and Vocabulary

Associative Properties:

$(a + b) + c = a + (b + c)$

$(a \cdot b) \cdot c = a \cdot (b \cdot c)$

Commutative Properties:

$a + b = b + a$

$a \cdot b = b \cdot a$

Distributive Property:

$a(b + c) = ab + ac$

$a(b - c) = ab - ac$

Identity Properties:

$a + 0 = 0 + a = a$

$a \cdot 1 = 1 \cdot a = a$

Inverse Properties:

$a + (-a) = -a + a = 0$

$a \cdot \dfrac{1}{a} = \dfrac{1}{a} \cdot a = 1, a \neq 0$

Multiplication Properties of 0 and −1:

$a \cdot 0 = 0 \cdot a = 0$

$a \cdot (-1) = (-1) \cdot a = -a$

So many properties

Skill Examples

Identify the property illustrated.

1. $-2 \cdot (7 \cdot 5) = -2 \cdot (5 \cdot 7)$

Commutative Property of Multiplication

2. $(-8) \cdot 1 = -8$

Identity Property of Multiplication

3. $3(6x + 2) = 18x + 6$

Distributive Property

4. $(w + 3) + 7 = w + (3 + 7)$

Associative Property of Addition

PRACTICE MAKES *PURR*-FECT®

Check your answers at BigIdeasMath.com.

Identify the property illustrated.

5. $(9 \cdot 4) \cdot 5 = 9 \cdot (4 \cdot 5)$

_____

6. $(-1) \cdot (-12) = 12$

_____

7. $2a + (-2a) = 0$

_____

8. $0 + 11c = 11c$

_____

9. $9m \cdot 0 = 0$

_____

10. $(5 - 2b) + 3 = (-2b + 5) + 3$

_____

11. $7n - 4n = (7 - 4)n$

_____

12. $\dfrac{1}{15d} \cdot 15d = 1$

_____

13. $x + (y + 6) = (x + y) + 6$

_____

14. $\left(\dfrac{1}{16}k\right)(-32) = (-32)\left(\dfrac{1}{16}k\right)$

_____

REVIEW: Properties of Equality

Name _____

Key Concept and Vocabulary

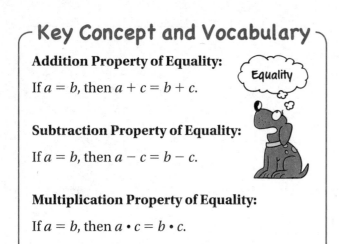

Addition Property of Equality:

If $a = b$, then $a + c = b + c$.

Subtraction Property of Equality:

If $a = b$, then $a - c = b - c$.

Multiplication Property of Equality:

If $a = b$, then $a \cdot c = b \cdot c$.

Division Property of Equality:

If $a = b$, then $a \div c = b \div c, c \neq 0$.

Visual Model

If two sides of a scale weigh the same, the scale balances.

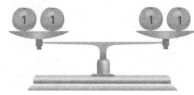

If you add or subtract the same amount on each side of the scale, the scale still balances.

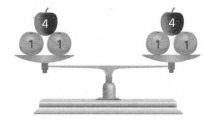

Skill Example

1. Solve $\dfrac{x}{4} - 3 = 7$.

$\dfrac{x}{4} - 3 = 7$	Write the equation.
$\underline{+3 \quad +3}$	Addition Property of Equality
$\dfrac{x}{4} = 10$	Simplify.
$\dfrac{x}{4} \cdot 4 = 10 \cdot 4$	Multiplication Property of Equality
$x = 40$	Simplify.

Application Example

2. Ski rental is $45 for 3 hours and $10 for each additional hour. You pay $75. Write and solve an equation to find the number of additional hours you rented the skis.

$10h + 45 = 75$	Write the equation.
$\underline{-45 \quad -45}$	Subtraction Property of Equality
$10h = 30$	Simplify.
$\dfrac{10h}{10} = \dfrac{30}{10}$	Division Property of Equality
$h = 3$	Simplify.

⋮⋰ You rented the skis for 3 additional hours.

PRACTICE MAKES *PURR-FECT*®

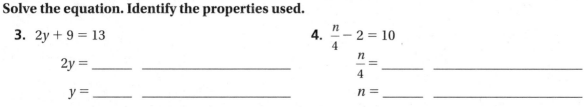

Check your answers at BigIdeasMath.com.

Solve the equation. Identify the properties used.

3. $2y + 9 = 13$

$2y =$ _____ _____

$y =$ _____ _____

4. $\dfrac{n}{4} - 2 = 10$

$\dfrac{n}{4} =$ _____ _____

$n =$ _____ _____

5. **COMPUTER** You pay $87 to get your computer repaired. You are charged $37 for parts and $20 per hour of labor. Write and solve an equation to find the number of labor hours you were charged. _____

92   Skills Review Topic 17.2

REVIEW: Properties of Inequality

Name _____

Key Concept and Vocabulary

Addition Properties of Inequality:

If $a > b$, then $a + c > b + c$.

If $a < b$, then $a + c < b + c$.

Subtraction Properties of Inequality:

If $a > b$, then $a - c > b - c$.

If $a < b$, then $a - c < b - c$.

Multiplication and Division Properties of Inequality when $c > 0$:

If $a > b$, then $a \cdot c > b \cdot c$.

If $a < b$, then $a \cdot c < b \cdot c$.

If $a > b$, then $\dfrac{a}{c} > \dfrac{b}{c}$.

If $a < b$, then $\dfrac{a}{c} < \dfrac{b}{c}$.

Multiplication and Division Properties of Inequality when $c < 0$:

If $a > b$, then $a \cdot c < b \cdot c$.

If $a < b$, then $a \cdot c > b \cdot c$.

If $a > b$, then $\dfrac{a}{c} < \dfrac{b}{c}$.

If $a < b$, then $\dfrac{a}{c} > \dfrac{b}{c}$.

Inequalities

Skill Examples

1. Solve $\dfrac{x}{4} + 2 > 12$.

$\dfrac{x}{4} + 2 > 12$	Write the equation.
$\underline{-2 \quad -2}$	Subtraction Property of Inequality
$\dfrac{x}{4} > 10$	Simplify.
$\dfrac{x}{4} \cdot 4 > 10 \cdot 4$	Multiplication Property of Inequality
$x > 40$	Simplify.

2. Solve $-7v - 21 \le 28$.

$-7v - 21 \le 28$	Write the equation.
$\underline{+21 \quad +21}$	Addition Property of Inequality
$-7v \le 49$	Simplify.
$\dfrac{-7v}{-7} \ge \dfrac{49}{-7}$	Division Property of Inequality. Reverse the inequality symbol.
$v \ge -7$	Simplify.

PRACTICE MAKES *PURR-FECT*®

Check your answers at BigIdeasMath.com.

Solve the inequality. Identify the properties used.

3. $3x - 5 \ge 4$

$3x\ \boxed{}$ ____ _____

$x\ \boxed{}$ ____ _____

4. $1 - \dfrac{m}{2} < 3$

$-\dfrac{m}{2}\ \boxed{}$ ____ _____

$m\ \boxed{}$ ____ _____

Write and solve an inequality that represents the value of x.

5. Area > 44 ft²

8 ft

$(x + 2)$ ft

_____

_____

6. Area ≤ 64 m²

$(5 - x)$ m

16 m

_____

_____

REVIEW: Properties of Exponents

Name _____

Key Concept and Vocabulary

Product of Powers Property:

$a^m \cdot a^n = a^{m+n}$

Power of a Power Property

$\left(a^m\right)^n = a^{mn}$

Power of Quotient Property:

$\left(\dfrac{a}{b}\right)^m = \dfrac{a^m}{b^m}$, where $b \neq 0$

Zero Exponents

$a^0 = 1$, where $a \neq 0$

Quotient of Powers Property:

$\dfrac{a^m}{a^n} = a^{m-n}$, where $a \neq 0$

Power of a Product Property

$(ab)^m = a^m b^m$

Negative Exponents:

$a^{-n} = \dfrac{1}{a^n}$, where $a \neq 0$

Skill Examples

1. $x^2 \cdot x^4 = x^{2+4} = x^6$

2. $\left(w^5\right)^3 = w^{5\cdot 3} = w^{15}$

3. $\dfrac{y^6}{y^6} = y^{6-6} = y^0 = 1$

4. $\left(\dfrac{c}{2}\right)^3 = \dfrac{c^3}{2^3} = \dfrac{c^3}{8}$

5. $4g^{-3} = \dfrac{4}{g^3}$

Application Example

6. Write the area of the circle as a monomial.

    Area $= \pi r^2$

    $\qquad = \pi\left(2x^2\right)^2$

    $\qquad = \pi\left(2^2\right)\left(x^2\right)^2$

    $\qquad = 4\pi x^4$

    The area of the circle is $4\pi x^4$ square units.

    $2x^2$

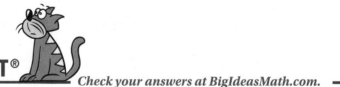

PRACTICE MAKES *PURR-FECT*®

Check your answers at BigIdeasMath.com.

Simplify the expression using only positive exponents.

7. $\dfrac{v^7}{v^4} =$ _____

8. $\left(q^2\right)^5 =$ _____

9. $r^3 \cdot r^3 =$ _____

10. $(3h)^3 =$ _____

11. $\left(\dfrac{5}{x^2}\right)^2 =$ _____

12. $\left(2k^{-3}\right)^2 =$ _____

13. **CUBE** Write the volume of the cube as a monomial.

    $V =$ _____

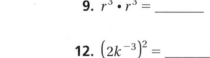

$4x^2$

$4x^2$

$4x^2$

REVIEW: Describing Linear Patterns

Name _____

Key Concept and Vocabulary

Equation: $y = 2x + 3$

Table:

x	0	1	2	3	4	5
y	3	5	7	9	11	13

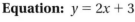

Linear patterns

Words: Each time x increases by 1, y increases by 2.

Visual Model

Moving to the right, each bar increases by 2 units.

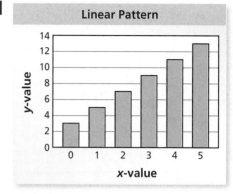

Skill Example

1. Equation: $y = 15 - 3x$

Table:

x	0	1	2	3	4	5
y	15	12	9	6	3	0

Words: Each time x increases by 1, y decreases by 3.

Application Example

2. The equation $P = 5t$ describes how much pay P (in dollars) you earn for working t hours. Make a table and describe the pattern.

t	1	2	3	4	5	6
P	5	10	15	20	25	30

You get paid $5 an hour.

PRACTICE MAKES PURR-FECT®

Check your answers at BigIdeasMath.com.

Complete the table. Then describe the pattern.

3. $y = x + 7$

x	0	1	2	3	4	5
y						

_____

_____

4. $y = 9 - x$

x	0	1	2	3	4	5
y						

_____

_____

5. $y = 4x + 5$

x	0	1	2	3	4	5
y						

_____

_____

6. $y = 90 - 6x$

x	0	1	2	3	4	5
y						

_____

_____

Write an equation for the pattern.

7.

x	0	1	2	3	4	5
y	5	14	23	32	41	50

_____

8.

x	0	1	2	3	4	5
y	50	40	30	20	10	0

_____

9. HOURLY PAY The equation $P = 7t$ describes how much pay P (in dollars) you earn for working t hours. Describe the pattern. _____

REVIEW: Function Rules

Name _____

Key Concept and Vocabulary

Function Rule: $y = 2x + 4$

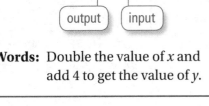

output   input

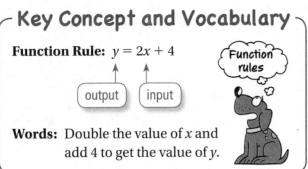

Words: Double the value of x and add 4 to get the value of y.

Visual Model

You can see how x and y compare by making an Input-Output table.

Function Rule: $y = 2x + 4$

Input, x	0	1	2	3	4	5
Output, y	4	6	8	10	12	14

Skill Example

1. **Function Rule:** $y = 20 - 4x$

   Input-Output Table:

Input, x	0	1	2	3	4	5
Output, y	20	16	12	8	4	0

   Words: Multiply the value of x by 4 and subtract from 20 to get the value of y.

Application Example

2. The equation $F = \frac{9}{5}C + 32$ describes how the Fahrenheit and Celsius scales relate. Describe this in words.

Input, C	0	5	10	15	20	25
Output, F	32	41	50	59	68	77

   ⋮⋮ Multiply C by $\frac{9}{5}$ and add 32 to get F.

PRACTICE MAKES *PURR*-FECT®

Check your answers at BigIdeasMath.com. ━━

Complete the table. Then describe the pattern.

3. $y = 2x + 6$

Input, x	0	1	2	3	4	5
Output, y						

_____

4. $y = 16 - 2x$

Input, x	0	1	2	3	4	5
Output, y						

_____

5. $y = 3x + 7$

Input, x	0	1	2	3	4	5
Output, y						

_____

6. $y = 65 - 10x$

Input, x	0	1	2	3	4	5
Output, y						

_____

UNIT CONVERSION **Complete the table and describe the function rule in words.**

7. Inches to Centimeters: $C = 2.54I$

Input, I	0	1	2	3	4	5
Output, C						

8. Miles to Kilometers: $K = 1.6M$

Input, M	0	1	2	3	4	5
Output, K						

_____

REVIEW: Graphs of Proportional Relationships

Name _____

Key Concept and Vocabulary

constant of proportionality

x and y are proportional. $\quad y = kx$

output

input

Proportional relationships

Visual Model

For positive values of x and y, as x increases, y increases.

$$y = \frac{1}{2}x$$

through origin

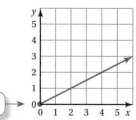

Skill Example

1. **Equation:** $y = 2x$

   Table:

x	0	1	2	3
y	0	2	4	6

   Graph:

   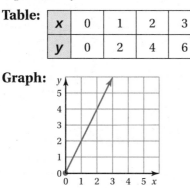

Application Example

2. The table shows the amount y (in gallons) of gasoline that a car uses to travel x miles. Graph the relationship.

x	y
20	1
40	2
60	3

   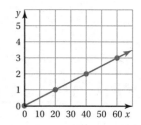

   ∴ x and y are proportional.

PRACTICE MAKES PURR-FECT®

Check your answers at BigIdeasMath.com.

Complete the table. Then sketch the graph.

3. $y = 1.5x$

x	y
0	
1	
2	
3	
4	

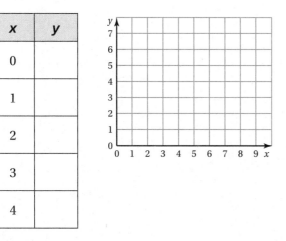

4. $y = \dfrac{2}{3}x$

x	y
0	
1	
2	
3	
4	

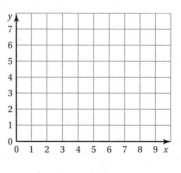

5. **WALRUS** The amount y that a walrus eats is proportional to its weight x. A 4000-pound walrus eats 20 pounds each day. How much does a 2000-pound walrus eat each day? _____

REVIEW: Graphs of Equations

Name _____

Key Concept and Vocabulary

Equation: $y = 3 - \frac{3}{4}x$

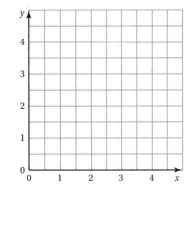

Visual Model

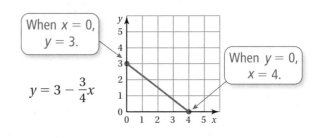

When $x = 0$, $y = 3$.

When $y = 0$, $x = 4$.

$y = 3 - \frac{3}{4}x$

Skill Example

1. Equation: $y = 3 - \frac{3}{4}x$

   Table:

x	0	1	2	3	4	5
y	3	$\frac{9}{4}$	$\frac{3}{2}$	$\frac{3}{4}$	0	$-\frac{3}{4}$

Application Example

2. A parachutist's height h (in feet) is given by $h = 450 - 15t$, where t is the time in seconds. When does the parachutist land?

t	0	5	10	15	20	25	30
h	450	375	300	225	150	75	0

   After 30 seconds, the height is 0 feet.

PRACTICE MAKES PURR-FECT®

Check your answers at BigIdeasMath.com.

Complete the table. Then sketch the graph.

3. $y = 4 - x$

x	y
0	
1	
2	
3	
4	

4. $y = \frac{1}{2}x + 2$

x	y
0	
1	
2	
3	
4	

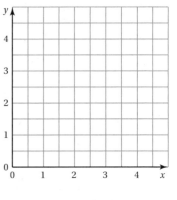

Find the x-intercept and y-intercept of the graph of the equation.

5. $y = 5 - x$ x-intercept = _____

   y-intercept = _____

6. $y = 5 - \frac{1}{2}x$ x-intercept = _____

   y-intercept = _____

7. **PARACHUTE FALL** A parachutist's height h (in feet) is given by $h = 1000 - 20t$, where t is the time in seconds. When does the parachutist land?

   _____

REVIEW: Independent and Dependent Variables

Name _____

Key Concept and Vocabulary

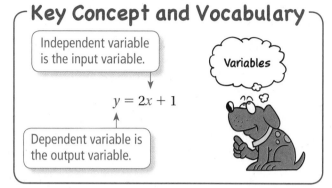

Independent variable is the input variable.

$$y = 2x + 1$$

Dependent variable is the output variable.

Variables

Visual Model

Independent Variable	Expression	Dependent Variable
x	$2x + 1$	y
1	$2(1) + 1$	3
2	$2(2) + 1$	5
3	$2(3) + 1$	7

Skill Examples

1. In $y = 3x - 2$, x is the independent variable and y is the dependent variable.

2. In $C = 2\pi r$, r is the independent variable and C is the dependent variable.

3. In $A = \ell w$, ℓ and w are the independent variables and A is the dependent variable.

Application Example

4. Your income i is calculated from the total time t worked. Identify the independent variable and the dependent variable.

   Total time t is the independent variable and your income i is the dependent variable.

PRACTICE MAKES *PURR*-FECT®

Check your answers at BigIdeasMath.com. ▬

Identify the independent variable(s) and the dependent variable.

5. $y = 6x + 1$ _____

6. $A = \dfrac{1}{2}bh$ _____

7. $A = \pi r^2$ _____

8. $m = 15 - n$ _____

9. $V = \ell wh$ _____

10. $P = 2\ell + 2w$ _____

11.

Hours Studying, h	Test Score, s
2	72%
3	80%
5	91%
7	98%

_____

12.

Number of CDs, n	Total Cost, c
1	$9.99
2	$19.98
3	$29.97
4	$39.96

_____

13. **DISTANCE** To find the distance d traveled, you multiply the rate r by the time t. Identify the independent variables and the dependent variable.

_____

Name _____

Key Concept and Vocabulary

$$\text{slope} = \frac{\text{rise}}{\text{run}} = \frac{\text{change in } y}{\text{change in } x} = \frac{y_2 - y_1}{x_2 - x_1}$$

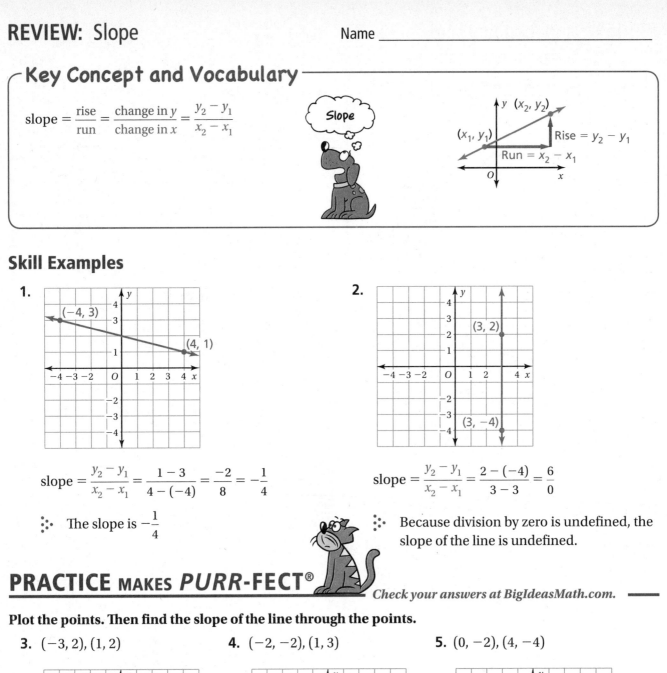

Slope

(x_1, y_1) (x_2, y_2)

Rise = $y_2 - y_1$

Run = $x_2 - x_1$

Skill Examples

1.

(−4, 3)

(4, 1)

$$\text{slope} = \frac{y_2 - y_1}{x_2 - x_1} = \frac{1 - 3}{4 - (-4)} = \frac{-2}{8} = -\frac{1}{4}$$

∴ The slope is $-\dfrac{1}{4}$

2.

(3, 2)

(3, −4)

$$\text{slope} = \frac{y_2 - y_1}{x_2 - x_1} = \frac{2 - (-4)}{3 - 3} = \frac{6}{0}$$

∴ Because division by zero is undefined, the slope of the line is undefined.

PRACTICE MAKES PURR-FECT®

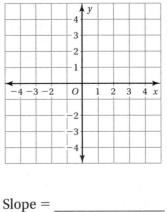

Check your answers at BigIdeasMath.com.

Plot the points. Then find the slope of the line through the points.

3. $(-3, 2), (1, 2)$

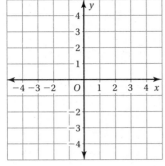

Slope = _____

4. $(-2, -2), (1, 3)$

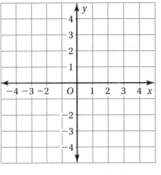

Slope = _____

5. $(0, -2), (4, -4)$

Slope = _____

REVIEW: Square Roots

Name _____

Key Concept and Vocabulary

A **square root** of a number p is a number whose square is equal to p. Every positive number has a positive *and* a negative square root. A **perfect square** is a number with integers as its square roots.

Positive Square Root: $\sqrt{9} = 3$

Negative Square Root: $-\sqrt{9} = -3$

Both Square Roots: $\pm\sqrt{9} = \pm3$

Square root

Skill Examples

1. $\sqrt{36}$

   ⋮• Because $6^2 = 36$, $\sqrt{36} = 6$.

2. $-\sqrt{144}$

   ⋮• Because $12^2 = 144$, $-\sqrt{144} = -12$.

3. $\pm\sqrt{3.24}$

   ⋮• Because $1.8^2 = 3.24$,

   $\pm\sqrt{3.24} = -1.8$ and 1.8.

Application Example

4. The area of a square table top is 256 square inches. What is the length of one side of the table top?

   $A = s^2$

   $256 = s^2$

   $\sqrt{256} = \sqrt{s^2}$

   $16 = s$

   ⋮• The length of one side of the table top is 16 inches.

PRACTICE MAKES *PURR-FECT*®

Check your answers at BigIdeasMath.com.

Find the square root(s).

5. $-\sqrt{64} = $ _____

6. $\sqrt{121} = $ _____

7. $\pm\sqrt{625} = $ _____

8. $\sqrt{4} = $ _____

9. $\pm\sqrt{289} = $ _____

10. $-\sqrt{196} = $ _____

11. $\sqrt{0.25} = $ _____

12. $-\sqrt{1.69} = $ _____

13. $\pm\sqrt{\dfrac{16}{49}} = $ _____

14. $-\sqrt{\dfrac{81}{100}} = $ _____

15. $\pm\sqrt{2.25} = $ _____

16. $\sqrt{\dfrac{9}{400}} = $ _____

Evaluate the expression.

17. $8\sqrt{9} - 5 = $ _____

18. $7 + 10\sqrt{\dfrac{1}{25}} = $ _____

19. $\sqrt{\dfrac{24}{6}} + 3 = $ _____

20. $6.2 + \sqrt{6.76} = $ _____

21. $7\left(\sqrt{400} - 9\right) = $ _____

22. $2\left(\sqrt{\dfrac{147}{3}} - 1\right) = $ _____

23. **ROOM** The area of the floor of a square room is 441 square feet. What is the length of one side of the floor of the room?

_____

REVIEW: Approximating Square Roots

Name _____

Key Concept and Vocabulary

To approximate a square root to the nearest integer, use a number line and the square roots of the perfect squares nearest to the number. Then determine which perfect square is closer to the radicand.

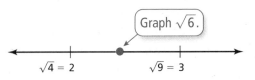
Approximating

Visual Model

Graph $\sqrt{6}$.

$\sqrt{4} = 2$ $\sqrt{9} = 3$

$\sqrt{6} \approx 2$ because 6 is closer to 4 than to 9.

Skill Example

1. $\sqrt{29} \approx 5$

The nearest perfect square less than 29 is 25. The nearest perfect square greater than 29 is 36. Because 29 is closer to 25 than to 36, $\sqrt{29}$ is closer to 5 than to 6.

Graph $\sqrt{29}$.

$\sqrt{25} = 5$ $\sqrt{36} = 6$

PRACTICE MAKES *PURR*-FECT®

Check your answers at BigIdeasMath.com.

Estimate to the nearest integer.

2. $\sqrt{60} \approx$ _____

3. $\sqrt{14} \approx$ _____

4. $\sqrt{86} \approx$ _____

5. $\sqrt{19} \approx$ _____

6. $\sqrt{77} \approx$ _____

7. $\sqrt{138} \approx$ _____

8. $-\sqrt{45} \approx$ _____

9. $-\sqrt{103} \approx$ _____

Graph the two numbers. Then compare them using < or >.

10. $5 \;\square\; \sqrt{5}$ ⟵——————⟶

11. $3\frac{1}{4} \;\square\; \sqrt{13}$ ⟵——————⟶

12. $\sqrt{20} \;\square\; 4\frac{4}{5}$ ⟵——————⟶

13. $\sqrt{47} \;\square\; 6.1$ ⟵——————⟶

14. $9.3 \;\square\; \sqrt{96}$ ⟵——————⟶

15. $-3.5 \;\square\; -\sqrt{15}$ ⟵——————⟶

16. PLATE The radius of a circle with area A is approximately $\sqrt{\dfrac{A}{3}}$. The area of a plate is 81 square inches. Estimate the radius of the plate to the nearest inch. _____

17. DECK The area of a square deck is 248 square feet. Estimate the length of one side of the deck to the nearest foot. _____

REVIEW: Adding and Subtracting Square Root Expressions

Name _____

Key Concept and Vocabulary

You can add or subtract radical expressions the same way you combine like terms, such as $5x + 4x = 9x$.

Adding and subtracting

Adding: $5\sqrt{3} + 4\sqrt{3} = 9\sqrt{3}$

Subtracting: $5\sqrt{3} - 4\sqrt{3} = \sqrt{3}$

Skill Examples

1. $12\sqrt{5} + 4\sqrt{5} = (12 + 4)\sqrt{5}$
$$= 16\sqrt{5}$$

2. $9\sqrt{10} - 7\sqrt{10} = (9 - 7)\sqrt{10}$
$$= 2\sqrt{10}$$

Application Example

3. What is the perimeter of the triangle?

Perimeter $= 10\sqrt{6} + 13\sqrt{6} + 6\sqrt{6}$
$$= (10 + 13 + 6)\sqrt{6}$$
$$= 29\sqrt{6}$$

$10\sqrt{6}$ $13\sqrt{6}$

$6\sqrt{6}$

PRACTICE MAKES PURR-FECT®

Check your answers at BigIdeasMath.com.

Simplify the expression.

4. $5\sqrt{7} + 4\sqrt{7} =$ _____

5. $15\sqrt{17} - 6\sqrt{17} =$ _____

6. $2\sqrt{14} + 3\sqrt{14} =$ _____

7. $7\sqrt{26} + 11\sqrt{26} =$ _____

8. $9.5\sqrt{6} - 5.6\sqrt{6} =$ _____

9. $1.6\sqrt{13} + 3.8\sqrt{13} =$ _____

10. $2\sqrt{5} - 7\sqrt{5} =$ _____

11. $\frac{7}{4}\sqrt{15} - \frac{3}{4}\sqrt{15} =$ _____

12. $\frac{11}{8}\sqrt{11} + \frac{5}{8}\sqrt{11} =$ _____

Find the perimeter of the figure.

13.

$4\sqrt{17}$ $3\sqrt{17}$

$5\sqrt{17}$

Perimeter = _____

14.

$6\sqrt{13}$ $6\sqrt{13}$

$9\sqrt{13}$

Perimeter = _____

15.

$6\sqrt{2}$

$15\sqrt{2}$

$9\sqrt{2}$

$12\sqrt{2}$

Perimeter = _____

16.

$10\sqrt{7}$

$15\sqrt{7}$ $17\sqrt{7}$

$18\sqrt{7}$

Perimeter = _____

REVIEW: Simplifying Square Roots

Name _____

Key Concept and Vocabulary

Product Property of Square Roots

Algebra: $\sqrt{xy} = \sqrt{x} \cdot \sqrt{y}$, where $x, y \geq 0$

Numbers: $\sqrt{12} = \sqrt{4 \cdot 3} = \sqrt{4} \cdot \sqrt{3} = 2\sqrt{3}$

Quotient Property of Square Roots

Algebra: $\sqrt{\dfrac{x}{y}} = \dfrac{\sqrt{x}}{\sqrt{y}}$, where $x \geq 0$ and $y > 0$

Numbers: $\sqrt{\dfrac{7}{9}} = \dfrac{\sqrt{7}}{\sqrt{9}} = \dfrac{\sqrt{7}}{3}$

Skill Examples

1. $\sqrt{18} = \sqrt{9 \cdot 2}$

   $\quad = \sqrt{9} \cdot \sqrt{2}$

   $\quad = 3\sqrt{2}$

2. $\sqrt{75} = \sqrt{25 \cdot 3}$

   $\quad = \sqrt{25} \cdot \sqrt{3}$

   $\quad = 5\sqrt{3}$

3. $\sqrt{\dfrac{5}{36}} = \dfrac{\sqrt{5}}{\sqrt{36}}$

   $\quad = \dfrac{\sqrt{5}}{6}$

Application Example

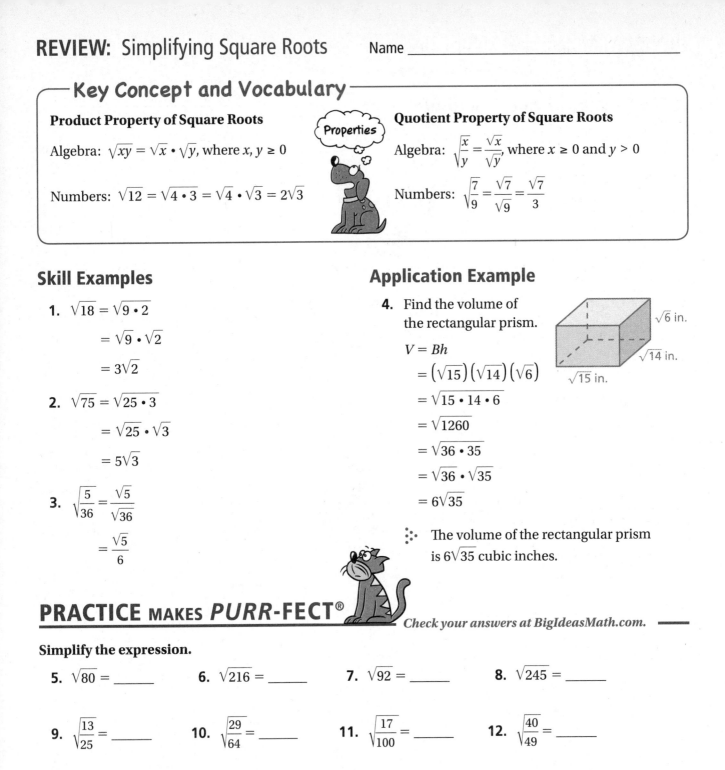

4. Find the volume of the rectangular prism.

   $V = Bh$

   $\quad = \left(\sqrt{15}\right)\left(\sqrt{14}\right)\left(\sqrt{6}\right)$

   $\quad = \sqrt{15 \cdot 14 \cdot 6}$

   $\quad = \sqrt{1260}$

   $\quad = \sqrt{36 \cdot 35}$

   $\quad = \sqrt{36} \cdot \sqrt{35}$

   $\quad = 6\sqrt{35}$

   The volume of the rectangular prism is $6\sqrt{35}$ cubic inches.

PRACTICE MAKES *PURR-FECT*®

Check your answers at BigIdeasMath.com.

Simplify the expression.

5. $\sqrt{80} =$ _____

6. $\sqrt{216} =$ _____

7. $\sqrt{92} =$ _____

8. $\sqrt{245} =$ _____

9. $\sqrt{\dfrac{13}{25}} =$ _____

10. $\sqrt{\dfrac{29}{64}} =$ _____

11. $\sqrt{\dfrac{17}{100}} =$ _____

12. $\sqrt{\dfrac{40}{49}} =$ _____

Find the volume of the rectangular prism.

13.

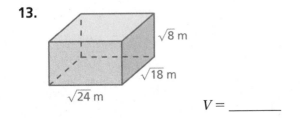

$V =$ _____

14.

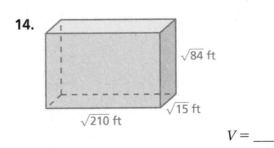

$V =$ _____

REVIEW: Pythagorean Theorem

Name _____

Key Concept and Vocabulary

In any right triangle,

a and b are leg lengths.

$$a^2 + b^2 = c^2.$$

c is the length of the hypotenuse.

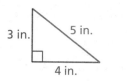
Pythagorean Theorem

Visual Model

3 in.   5 in.
4 in.

$$3^2 + 4^2 = 5^2$$

Skill Examples

1. $a^2 + b^2 = c^2$

   $6^2 + 8^2 = c^2$

   $100 = c^2$

   $10 \text{ cm} = c$

   c   6 cm
   8 cm

2. $a^2 + b^2 = c^2$

   $5^2 + b^2 = 13^2$

   $b^2 = 144$

   $b = 12 \text{ ft}$

   5 ft
   13 ft   b

Application Example

3. The base of a ladder is 9 feet from a building. The ladder extends 12 feet up the side of the building. How long is the ladder?

   The ladder is the hypotenuse of a right triangle.

   $a^2 + b^2 = c^2$

   $9^2 + 12^2 = c^2$

   $225 = c^2$

   $15 = c$

   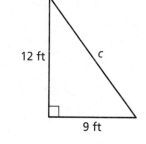
   12 ft   c
   9 ft

   ⋰ The ladder is 15 feet long.

PRACTICE MAKES *PURR-FECT*®

Check your answers at BigIdeasMath.com.

Find the missing length of the triangle.

4. 8 yd
   c   15 yd
   _____

5. 16 mm
   a   20 mm
   _____

6. 1 m $\frac{3}{5}$ m
   b
   _____

7. **RAMP** You make the skateboarding ramp shown. Find the height of the ramp. _____

   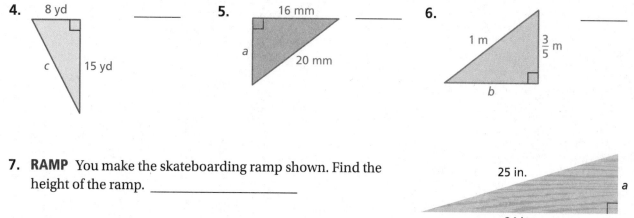
   25 in.   a
   24 in.

REVIEW: Cube Roots

Name _____

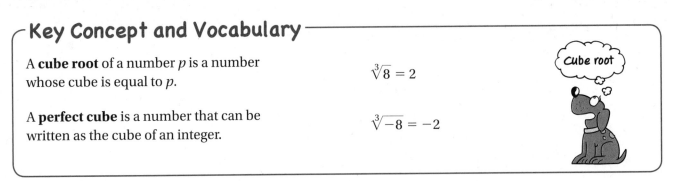
Skill Examples

1. $\sqrt[3]{1000}$

   ∴ Because $10^3 = 1000$, $\sqrt[3]{1000} = 10$.

2. $\sqrt[3]{-64}$

   ∴ Because $(-4)^3 = -64$, $\sqrt[3]{-64} = -4$.

3. $\sqrt[3]{\dfrac{1}{8}}$

   ∴ Because $\left(\dfrac{1}{2}\right)^3 = \dfrac{1}{8}$, $\sqrt[3]{\dfrac{1}{8}} = \dfrac{1}{2}$.

Application Example

4. The volume of a cube-shaped container is 512 cubic inches. What is the edge length of the container?

   $V = s^3$

   $512 = s^3$

   $\sqrt[3]{512} = \sqrt[3]{s^3}$

   $8 = s$

   ∴ The edge length of the container is 8 inches.

PRACTICE MAKES PURR-FECT®

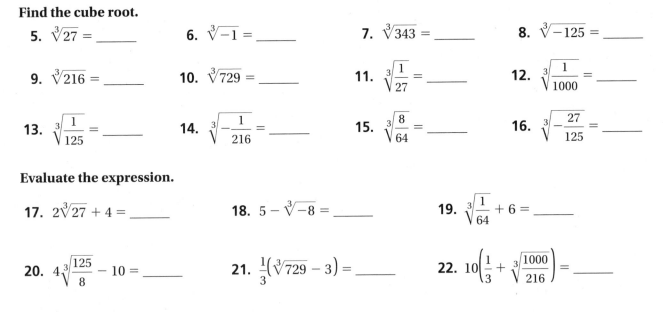

Check your answers at BigIdeasMath.com.

Find the cube root.

5. $\sqrt[3]{27} =$ _____

6. $\sqrt[3]{-1} =$ _____

7. $\sqrt[3]{343} =$ _____

8. $\sqrt[3]{-125} =$ _____

9. $\sqrt[3]{216} =$ _____

10. $\sqrt[3]{729} =$ _____

11. $\sqrt[3]{\dfrac{1}{27}} =$ _____

12. $\sqrt[3]{\dfrac{1}{1000}} =$ _____

13. $\sqrt[3]{\dfrac{1}{125}} =$ _____

14. $\sqrt[3]{-\dfrac{1}{216}} =$ _____

15. $\sqrt[3]{\dfrac{8}{64}} =$ _____

16. $\sqrt[3]{-\dfrac{27}{125}} =$ _____

Evaluate the expression.

17. $2\sqrt[3]{27} + 4 =$ _____

18. $5 - \sqrt[3]{-8} =$ _____

19. $\sqrt[3]{\dfrac{1}{64}} + 6 =$ _____

20. $4\sqrt[3]{\dfrac{125}{8}} - 10 =$ _____

21. $\dfrac{1}{3}\left(\sqrt[3]{729} - 3\right) =$ _____

22. $10\left(\dfrac{1}{3} + \sqrt[3]{\dfrac{1000}{216}}\right) =$ _____

23. **ROOM** The volume of a cube-shaped room is 729 cubic feet. You paint four walls of the room. How many square feet do you paint?

REVIEW: Metric Length

Name _____

Key Concept and Vocabulary

Two metric units of length are centimeters (cm) and meters (m).

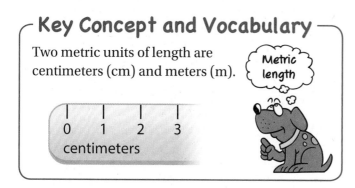

Visual Model

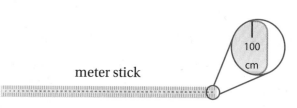

meter stick

There are 100 centimeters in 1 meter.

Skill Example

1.
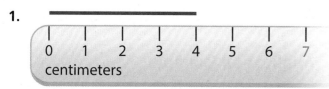

∴ The line is about 4 centimeters long.

Application Example

2. Measure the paper clip.

∴ The paper clip is about 3 centimeters long.

PRACTICE MAKES PURR-FECT®

Check your answers at BigIdeasMath.com.

Measure the line.

3.
about _____ centimeters

4.
about _____ centimeters

5.
about _____ centimeters

Find and measure the object in your classroom.

6.
about _____ centimeters

7.
about _____ meters

8. **BASKETBALL COURT** Your friend says that the length of a basketball court is about 28. Is the basketball court about 28 centimeters long or about 28 meters long?

_____

REVIEW: Customary Length

Name _____

Key Concept and Vocabulary

Three customary units of length are inches (in.), feet (ft), and yards (yd).

Visual Models

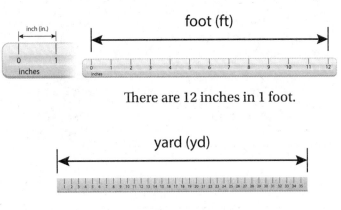

There are 12 inches in 1 foot.

There are 3 feet in 1 yard.

Skill Example

1.

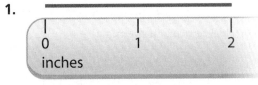

⋮ The line is about 2 inches long.

Application Example

2. Measure the screw.

⋮ The screw is about 3 inches long.

PRACTICE MAKES PURR-FECT®

Check your answers at BigIdeasMath.com.

Measure the line.

3. _____

about _____ inches

4. _____

about _____ inches

5. _____

about _____ inches

Find the object shown in your classroom. Choose an inch ruler, a yardstick, or a measuring tape to measure the object. Then measure.

6.

Tool: _____

Length: about _____

7.

Tool: _____

Length: about _____

REVIEW: Metric Capacity

Name _____

Key Concept and Vocabulary

Two metric units of capacity are milliliters (mL) and liters (L).

Metric capacity

Visual Models

20 drops of liquid from an eyedropper is about 1 milliliter.

There is about 1 liter of liquid in the water bottle.

1,000 milliliters = 1 liter

Skill Example

1.

1 liter

500 mL

There are 600 milliliters of liquid in the beaker.

Application Example

2. Does the pitcher contain 2 liters or 2 milliliters of lemonade?

The pitcher contains 2 liters of lemonade.

PRACTICE MAKES PURR-FECT®

Check your answers at BigIdeasMath.com.

Write the total liquid volume shown.

3.

4.

_____

_____

Choose the better estimate.

5.

5 mL   5 L

6.

MILK

473 mL   473 L

7.

1 mL   1 L

REVIEW: Customary Capacity

Name _____

Key Concept and Vocabulary

Four customary units of capacity are cups (c), pints (pt), quarts (qt), and gallons (gal).

Customary capacity

Visual Model

gallon

quart

pint

cup

1 gallon = 4 quarts
1 quart = 2 pints
1 pint = 2 cups

Skill Example

1.

2 CUPS

1 CUP

There are 2 cups of water in the measuring cup.

Application Example

2. Does the watering can contain 5 gallons or 5 cups of water?

⋰ The watering can contains 5 cups of water.

PRACTICE MAKES *PURR-FECT*®

Check your answers at BigIdeasMath.com.

Determine which capacity is greater.

3. 3 quarts or 3 pints

_____

4. 12 cups or 7 pints

_____

5. 5 quarts or 1 gallon

_____

Which units should you use to measure the capacity, *gallons* or *cups*?

6. _____

7. _____

Choose the better estimate.

8.

3 qt   3 gal

9.

2 c   2 qt

10.

1 c   1 pt

REVIEW: Mass

Name _____

Key Concept and Vocabulary

Two units of mass are grams (g) and kilograms (kg).

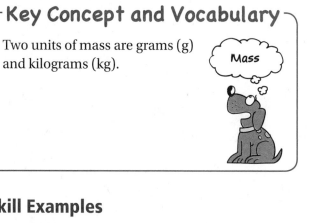

Visual Models

The mass of a paper clip is about 1 gram.

The mass of a baseball bat is about 1 kilogram.

Skill Examples

1. 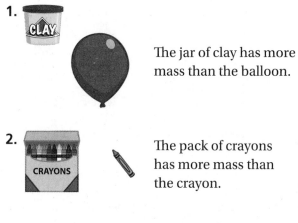 The jar of clay has more mass than the balloon.

2. The pack of crayons has more mass than the crayon.

Application Example

3. Is the mass of the nickel 5 grams or 5 kilograms?

   ⋮⋮ The mass of the nickel is 5 grams.

PRACTICE MAKES *PURR*-FECT®

Check your answers at BigIdeasMath.com.

Circle the object with the greater mass.

4.

5.

6.

Which units should you use to measure the mass, *grams* or *kilograms*? Explain.

7. _____
_____
_____

8.  _____
_____

Choose the better estimate.

9.   10.   11.

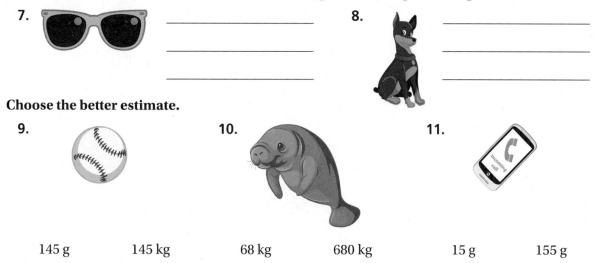

   145 g   145 kg   68 kg   680 kg   15 g   155 g

Name _____

Key Concept and Vocabulary

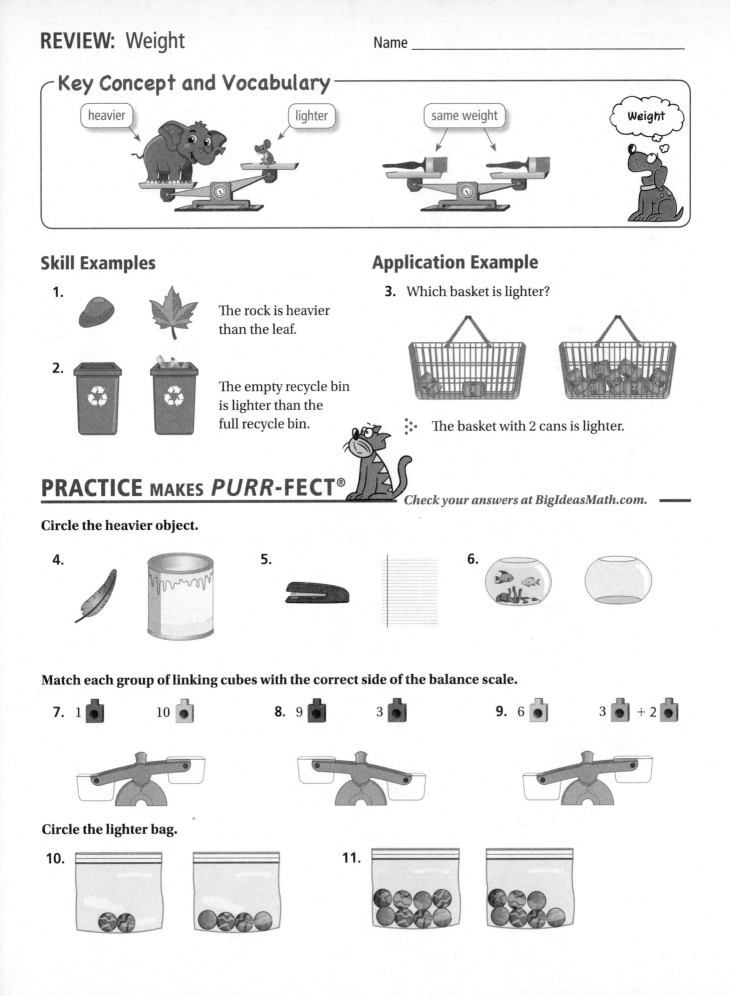

heavier   lighter   same weight   Weight

Skill Examples

1. The rock is heavier than the leaf.

2. The empty recycle bin is lighter than the full recycle bin.

Application Example

3. Which basket is lighter?

The basket with 2 cans is lighter.

PRACTICE MAKES *PURR-FECT*®

Check your answers at BigIdeasMath.com.

Circle the heavier object.

4.

5.

6.

Match each group of linking cubes with the correct side of the balance scale.

7. 1   10

8. 9   3

9. 6   3 + 2

Circle the lighter bag.

10.

11.

REVIEW: Converting Metric Units

Name _____

Key Concept and Vocabulary

Length
1 cm = 10 mm
1 m = 100 cm
1 km = 1,000 m

Volume
1 L = 1,000 mL
1 kL = 1,000 L
$1 \text{ cm}^3 = 1$ mL
$1 \text{ L} = 1,000 \text{ cm}^3$
$1 \text{ m}^3 = 1,000$ L
$1 \text{ m}^3 = 1,000,000 \text{ cm}^3$

Weight (Mass)
1 g = 1,000 mg
1 kg = 1,000 g

Metric units

Visual Model

1 L = 1,000 mL

Skill Examples

1. Convert 3 meters to centimeters.

   $3 \times 100 = 300$

   ⋮• There are 300 centimeters in 3 meters.

2. Convert 1,500 milliliters to liters.

   $1,500 \div 1,000 = 1.5$

   ⋮• There are 1.5 liters in 1,500 milliliters.

Application Example

3. A runner is running in a 5-kilometer race. How many meters long is the race?

   $5 \times 1,000 = 5,000$

   ⋮• The race is 5,000 meters long.

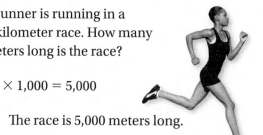

PRACTICE MAKES *PURR*-FECT®

Check your answers at BigIdeasMath.com. ▬

Complete the unit conversion.

4. 2 km = _____ m

5. 30 cm = _____ mm

6. 6 m = _____ cm

7. 0.5 m = _____ cm

8. 9 m = _____ mm

9. 7 kg = _____ g

10. 1.5 kg = _____ g

11. 2 L = _____ mL

12. 3.5 L = _____ mL

13. 300 cm = _____ m

14. 4,000 mL = _____ L

15. 1,250 g = _____ kg

Complete the unit conversion.

16.

10 cm

Salamander length = _____ mm

17.

2 m

Surfboard length = _____ cm

18.

4 m

Car length = _____ mm

19. **SPEED** An object moves 90 kilometers per hour. What is the speed of the object in meters per hour?

_____

REVIEW: Converting Customary Units   Name _____

Key Concept and Vocabulary

Length
1 ft = 12 in.
1 yd = 3 ft
1 mi = 1,760 yd
1 mi = 5,280 ft

Weight
1 lb = 16 oz
1 ton = 2,000 lb

Volume
1 Tbsp = 3 tsp
1 fl oz = 2 Tbsp
1 c = 16 Tbsp
1 c = 8 fl oz
1 pt = 2 c
1 qt = 2 pt
1 gal = 4 qt

Customary units

Visual Model

1 gallon = 4 quarts

Skill Examples

1. Convert 3 feet to inches.

   $3 \times 12 = 36$

   ⋮• There are 36 inches in 3 feet.

2. Convert 16 quarts to gallons.

   $16 \div 4 = 4$

   ⋮• There are 4 gallons in 16 quarts.

Application Example

3. An SUV weighs 2.5 tons, How many pounds does the SUV weigh?

   $2.5 \times 2,000 = 5,000$

   ⋮• The SUV weighs 5,000 pounds.

PRACTICE MAKES PURR-FECT®

Check your answers at BigIdeasMath.com. —

Complete the unit conversion.

4. 2 c = _____ fl oz

5. 4 ft = _____ in.

6. 3 T = _____ lb

7. 3 mi = _____ ft

8. $3\frac{1}{2}$ T = _____ lb

9. 2 gal = _____ pt

10. $4\frac{2}{3}$ yd = _____ ft

11. 5 pt = _____ fl oz

12. $3\frac{1}{4}$ qt = _____ c

13. 32 oz = _____ lb

14. 6 c = _____ qt

15. 64 fl oz = _____ gal

RECIPES Find the number of cups and the number of fluid ounces.

16.

_____ c = _____ fl oz

17.

_____ c = _____ fl oz

18.

_____ c = _____ fl oz

19. **SPEED** A parachutist falls at a speed of about $5\frac{2}{3}$ yards per second.

   Find this speed in feet per second. _____

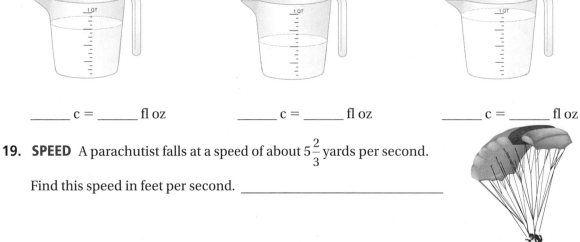

REVIEW: Converting Between Systems

Name _____

Key Concept and Vocabulary

Length
1 in. ≈ 2.54 cm
1 m ≈ 3.28 ft
1 mi ≈ 1.61 km

Capacity
1 qt ≈ 0.95 L
1 gal ≈ 3.79 L
1 c ≈ 237 mL
1 gal ≈ 3785 cm^3
1 m^3 ≈ 264 gal

Weight (Mass)
1 kg ≈ 2.2 lb
1 oz ≈ 28.3 g

Converstion factors

Visual Model

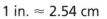

1 in. ≈ 2.54 cm

Skill Examples

1. $7 \text{ m} \approx 7 \text{ m} \cdot \dfrac{3.28 \text{ ft}}{1 \text{ m}} = 22.96 \text{ ft}$

2. $20 \text{ L} \approx 20 \text{ L} \cdot \dfrac{1 \text{ gal}}{3.79 \text{ L}} \approx 5.28 \text{ gal}$

3. $8 \text{ oz} \approx 8 \text{ oz} \cdot \dfrac{28.3 \text{ g}}{1 \text{ oz}} = 226.4 \text{ g}$

4. $2 \text{ c} \approx 2 \text{ c} \cdot \dfrac{237 \text{ mL}}{1 \text{ c}} = 474 \text{ mL}$

Application Example

5. A person is 63 inches tall. How many centimeters is that?

$$63 \text{ in.} \approx 63 \text{ in.} \cdot \dfrac{2.54 \text{ cm}}{1 \text{ in.}}$$

$$= 160.02 \text{ cm}$$

∴ The height of the person is about 160.02 centimeters.

PRACTICE MAKES *PURR*-FECT®

Check your answers at BigIdeasMath.com. —

Complete the unit conversion. Round to the nearest hundredth if necessary.

6. 26 mi ≈ _____ km

7. 150 g ≈ _____ oz

8. 2 L ≈ _____ qt

9. 70 lb ≈ _____ kg

10. 12 ft ≈ _____ m

11. 16 km ≈ _____ mi

12. 36 cm ≈ _____ in.

13. 7 gal ≈ _____ L

14. 9 qt ≈ _____ L

15. 800 mL ≈ _____ c

16. 5 gal ≈ _____ cm^3

17. 12 m^3 ≈ _____ gal

18. **WEIGHT** How much does the wolf weigh in pounds?

_____

Weight: 33 kg

19. **SPEED** A hummingbird flies at a speed of 33 feet per second. What is the speed of the hummingbird in meters per second?

_____

REVIEW: Telling Time to the Hour and Half Hour

Name _____

Key Concept and Vocabulary

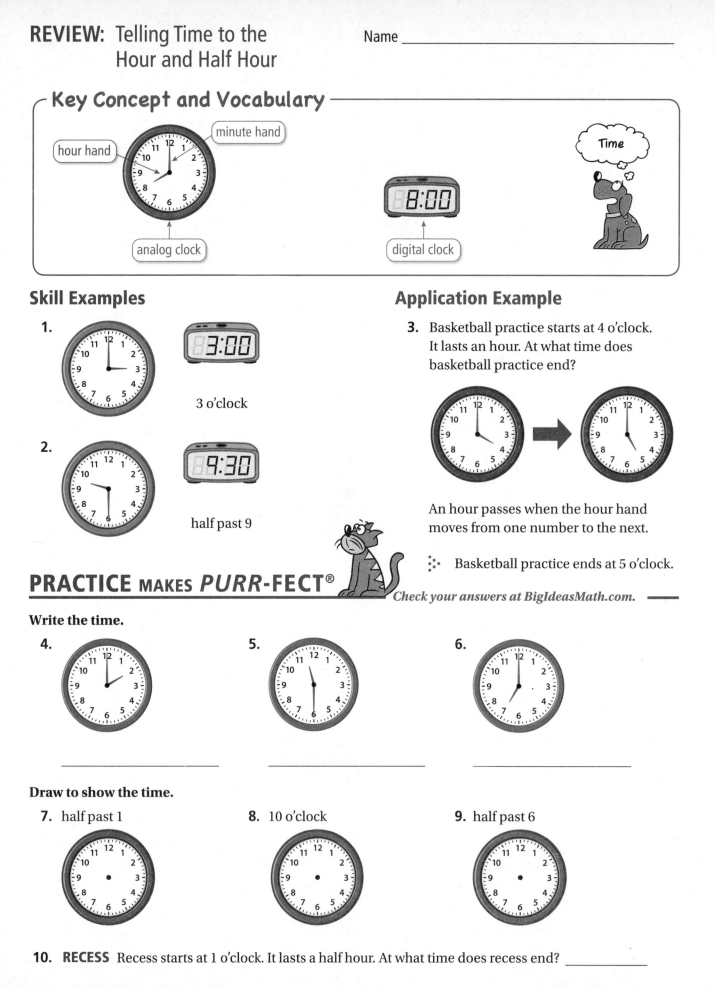

hour hand • minute hand • analog clock • digital clock • 8:00 • Time

Skill Examples

1. 3:00

   3 o'clock

2. 9:30

   half past 9

Application Example

3. Basketball practice starts at 4 o'clock. It lasts an hour. At what time does basketball practice end?

   An hour passes when the hour hand moves from one number to the next.

   ⋮ Basketball practice ends at 5 o'clock.

PRACTICE MAKES *PURR-FECT*®

Check your answers at BigIdeasMath.com.

Write the time.

4. _____

5. _____

6. _____

Draw to show the time.

7. half past 1

8. 10 o'clock

9. half past 6

10. **RECESS** Recess starts at 1 o'clock. It lasts a half hour. At what time does recess end? _____

REVIEW: Telling Time to the Nearest Minute

Name _____

Key Concept and Vocabulary

minute hand   hour hand   Time

Visual Model

1 minute

It takes 1 minute for the minute hand to move from one mark to the next.

Skill Examples

1.

1:28

28 minutes after 1

2.

7:57

3 minutes before 8

Application Example

3. You eat lunch at 12 minutes after 11. Show and write the time you eat lunch.

⋮ You eat lunch at 11:12.

PRACTICE MAKES *PURR*-FECT®

Check your answers at BigIdeasMath.com.

Write the time.

4.

5.

6.

Draw to show the time.

7. 2:22

8. 11:51

9. 21 minutes before 5

REVIEW: A.M. and P.M.

Name _____

Key Concept and Vocabulary

Morning

Evening

7:00 A.M.

7:00 P.M.

A.M. and P.M.

Skill Examples

1. Sunrise

5:35

(A.M.)   P.M.

2. Sunset

6:50

A.M.   (P.M.)

PRACTICE MAKES PURR-FECT®

Check your answers at BigIdeasMath.com.

Write the time. Circle *A.M.* or *P.M.*

3. Eat breakfast

A.M.   P.M.

4. Eat dinner

A.M.   P.M.

5. Do homework

A.M.   P.M.

6. Go to math class

A.M.   P.M.

Circle the earlier time.

7. 11:30 A.M.   11:30 P.M.

8. 2:25 P.M.   10:50 A.M.

9. 6:05 P.M.   1:40 P.M.

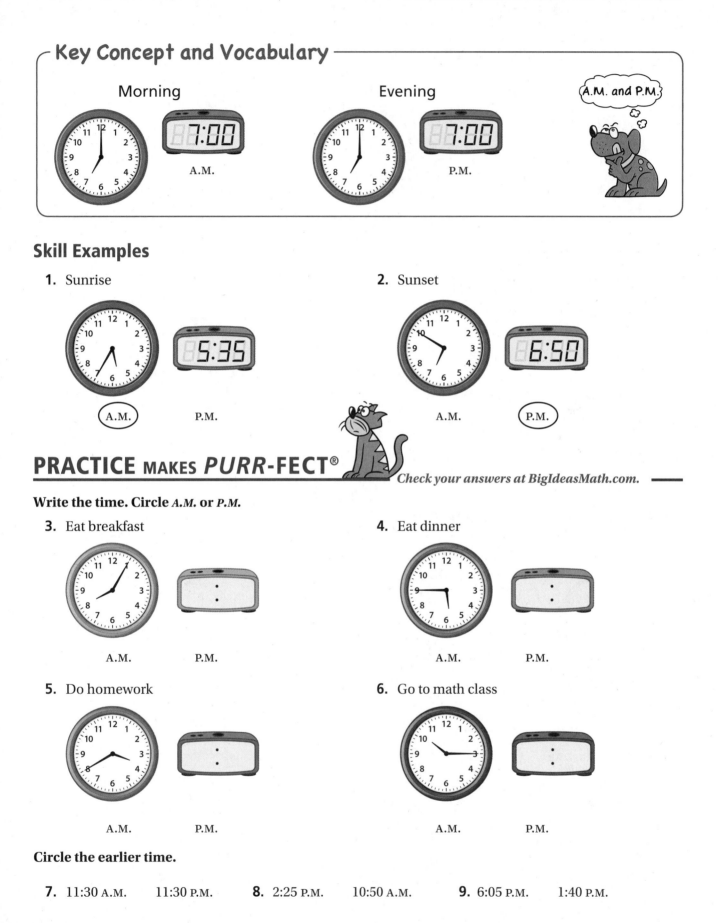

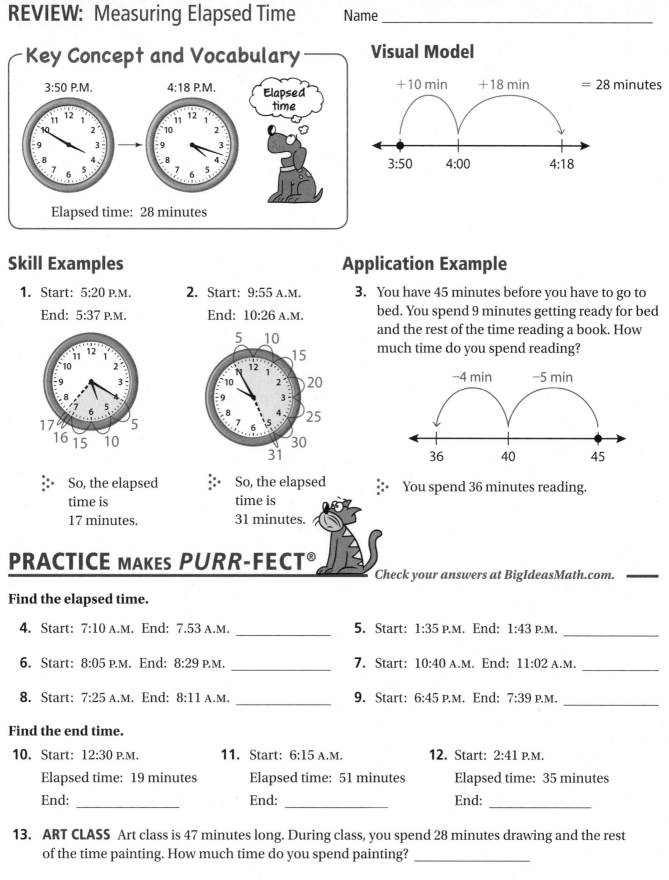

Key Concept and Vocabulary

3:50 P.M.   4:18 P.M.

Elapsed time

Elapsed time: 28 minutes

Visual Model

+10 min   +18 min   = 28 minutes

3:50   4:00   4:18

Skill Examples

1. Start: 5:20 P.M.
End: 5:37 P.M.

So, the elapsed time is 17 minutes.

2. Start: 9:55 A.M.
End: 10:26 A.M.

So, the elapsed time is 31 minutes.

Application Example

3. You have 45 minutes before you have to go to bed. You spend 9 minutes getting ready for bed and the rest of the time reading a book. How much time do you spend reading?

−4 min   −5 min

36   40   45

You spend 36 minutes reading.

PRACTICE MAKES PURR-FECT®

Check your answers at BigIdeasMath.com.

Find the elapsed time.

4. Start: 7:10 A.M. End: 7.53 A.M. _____

5. Start: 1:35 P.M. End: 1:43 P.M. _____

6. Start: 8:05 P.M. End: 8:29 P.M. _____

7. Start: 10:40 A.M. End: 11:02 A.M. _____

8. Start: 7:25 A.M. End: 8:11 A.M. _____

9. Start: 6:45 P.M. End: 7:39 P.M. _____

Find the end time.

10. Start: 12:30 P.M.
Elapsed time: 19 minutes
End: _____

11. Start: 6:15 A.M.
Elapsed time: 51 minutes
End: _____

12. Start: 2:41 P.M.
Elapsed time: 35 minutes
End: _____

13. **ART CLASS** Art class is 47 minutes long. During class, you spend 28 minutes drawing and the rest of the time painting. How much time do you spend painting? _____

14. **GAMES** You play a board game from 12:20 P.M. to 12:58 P.M. You stop and eat lunch. Then you play a video game from 1:26 P.M. to 2:18 P.M. How long do you play games in all? _____

Name _____

Key Concept and Vocabulary

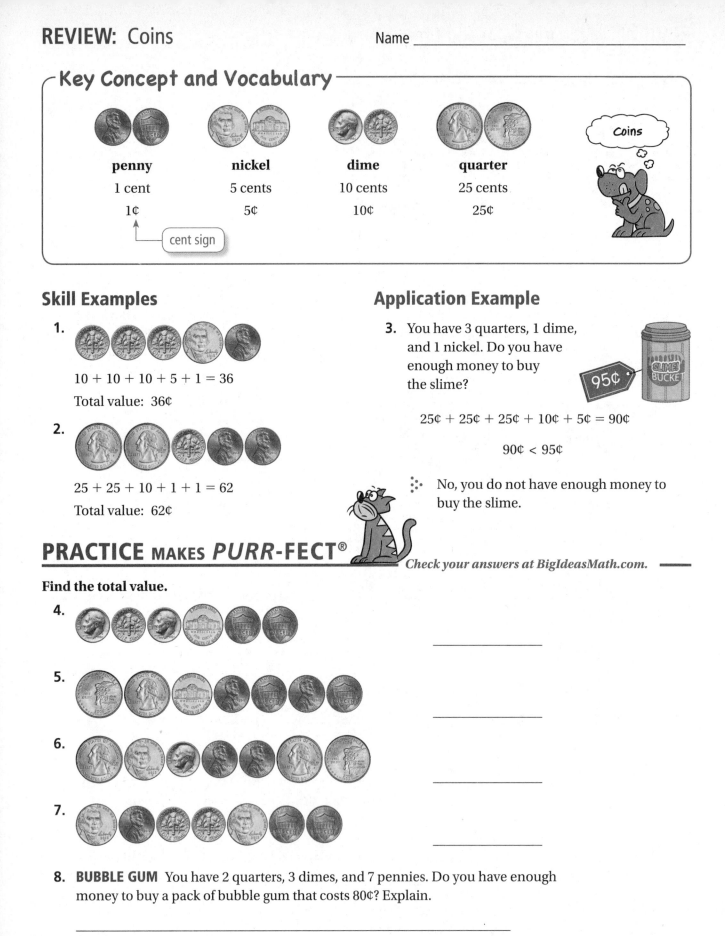

penny
1 cent
1¢ ← cent sign

nickel
5 cents
5¢

dime
10 cents
10¢

quarter
25 cents
25¢

Coins

Skill Examples

1.

$10 + 10 + 10 + 5 + 1 = 36$

Total value: 36¢

2.

$25 + 25 + 10 + 1 + 1 = 62$

Total value: 62¢

Application Example

3. You have 3 quarters, 1 dime, and 1 nickel. Do you have enough money to buy the slime?

95¢ SLIME! BUCKET

$25¢ + 25¢ + 25¢ + 10¢ + 5¢ = 90¢$

$90¢ < 95¢$

No, you do not have enough money to buy the slime.

PRACTICE MAKES *PURR-FECT*®

Check your answers at BigIdeasMath.com.

Find the total value.

4. _____

5. _____

6. _____

7. _____

8. **BUBBLE GUM** You have 2 quarters, 3 dimes, and 7 pennies. Do you have enough money to buy a pack of bubble gum that costs 80¢? Explain.

_____

Name _____

Key Concept and Vocabulary

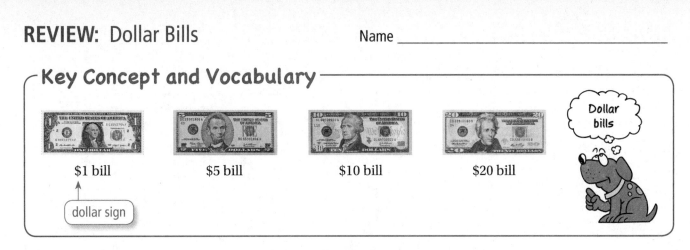

$1 bill $5 bill $10 bill $20 bill

dollar sign

Skill Example

1.

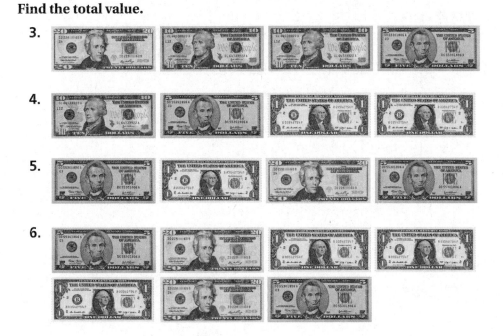

$20 + 10 + 5 + 1 = 36$

Total value: $36

Application Example

2. You have two $20 bills, three $10 bills, two $5 bills, and one $1 bill. Do you have enough money to buy a bicycle that costs $74?

$$20 + 20 + 10 + 10 + 10 + 5 + 5 + 1 = 81$$

$$\$81 > \$74$$

Yes, you have enough money to buy the bicycle.

PRACTICE MAKES *PURR-FECT*®

Check your answers at BigIdeasMath.com.

Find the total value.

3. _____

4. _____

5. _____

6. _____

7. **TELESCOPE** You have two $20 bills, one $10 bill, one $5 bill, and four $1 bills. Do you have enough money to buy a telescope that costs $69? Explain.

_____

REVIEW: Picture Graphs

Name _____

Key Concept and Vocabulary

Favorite Sport				
Basketball	☺	☺	☺	☺
Football	☺	☺	☺	
Soccer	☺	☺		

Each ☺ = 1 student.

> Three students chose football.

> The picture graphs represent the same survey.

Favorite Sport				
Basketball	☺	☺		
Football	☺	☾		
Soccer	☺			

Each ☺ = 2 students.

> Three students chose football.

Skill Example

1.

Favorite Type of Game App	
Action	ⵏⵏⵏ
Board	ⵏⵏⵏ I
Puzzle	III
Strategy	I

Favorite Type of Game App						
Action	☺	☺	☺	☺	☺	
Board	☺	☺	☺	☺	☺	☺
Puzzle	☺	☺	☺			
Strategy	☺					

Each ☺ = 1 student.

> The most favorite type of game app is board.

PRACTICE MAKES *PURR*-FECT®

Check your answers at BigIdeasMath.com.

2. Complete the picture graph.

Volunteer Jobs	
Clean	ⵏⵏⵏ II
Garden	II
Plant	IIII

Volunteer Jobs						
Clean						
Garden						
Plant						

Each ☺ = 1 volunteer.

FOOTBALL Use the picture graph.

3. Which team has the least number of wins? _____

4. How many more wins do the Hornets have than the Tigers? _____

5. How many wins do the Eagles and Hornets have in all? _____

6. **LOGIC** If ☺ ☾ = 6 on a picture graph, then what value does ☺ represent? Explain. _____

Team Wins					
Eagles	○	○	○	○	
Tigers	○	○	○		
Hornets	○	○	○	○	○

Each ○ = 1 win.

REVIEW: Bar Graphs

Name _____

Key Concept and Vocabulary

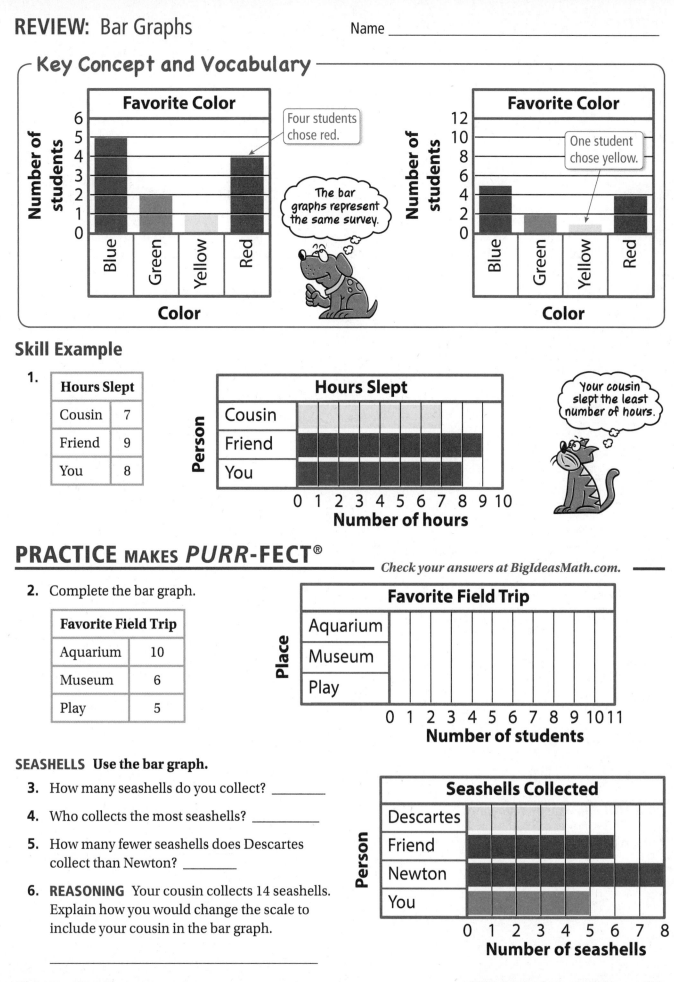

Favorite Color

Four students chose red.

The bar graphs represent the same survey.

Favorite Color

One student chose yellow.

Skill Example

1.

Hours Slept	
Cousin	7
Friend	9
You	8

Hours Slept

Your cousin slept the least number of hours.

PRACTICE MAKES *PURR*-FECT®

Check your answers at BigIdeasMath.com.

2. Complete the bar graph.

Favorite Field Trip	
Aquarium	10
Museum	6
Play	5

Favorite Field Trip

SEASHELLS Use the bar graph.

3. How many seashells do you collect? _____

4. Who collects the most seashells? _____

5. How many fewer seashells does Descartes collect than Newton? _____

6. **REASONING** Your cousin collects 14 seashells. Explain how you would change the scale to include your cousin in the bar graph.

_____

Seashells Collected

Key Concept and Vocabulary

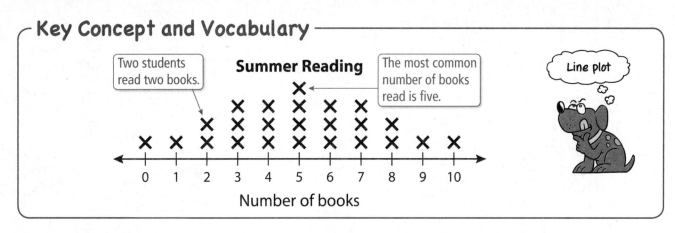

Summer Reading

Two students read two books.

The most common number of books read is five.

Line plot

Number of books

Skill Example

1.

Worm Lengths (centimeters)	
Worm 1	4
Worm 2	5
Worm 3	5
Worm 4	7
Worm 5	5
Worm 6	7

Worm Lengths

Number of centimeters

Application Example

2. What is the difference in height of the tallest giraffe and the shortest giraffe?

$17 - 14 = 3$

Giraffe Heights

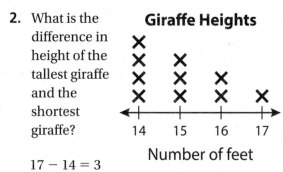

Number of feet

∴ The difference in height is 3 feet.

PRACTICE MAKES *PURR-FECT*®

Check your answers at BigIdeasMath.com.

3. Complete the line plot.

Baseball Bat Lengths (inches)	
Baseball bat 1	30
Baseball bat 2	26
Baseball bat 3	28
Baseball bat 4	32
Baseball bat 5	28
Baseball bat 6	34

Baseball Bat Lengths

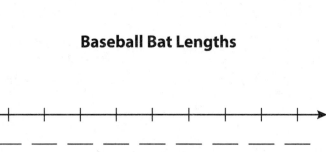

Number of inches

BASEBALL Use the line plot above.

4. What is the most common baseball bat length? _____

5. How many baseball bats are greater than 28 inches long? _____

6. What is the difference in length of the longest baseball bat and the shortest baseball bat? _____

REVIEW: Circle Graphs

Name _____

Key Concept and Vocabulary

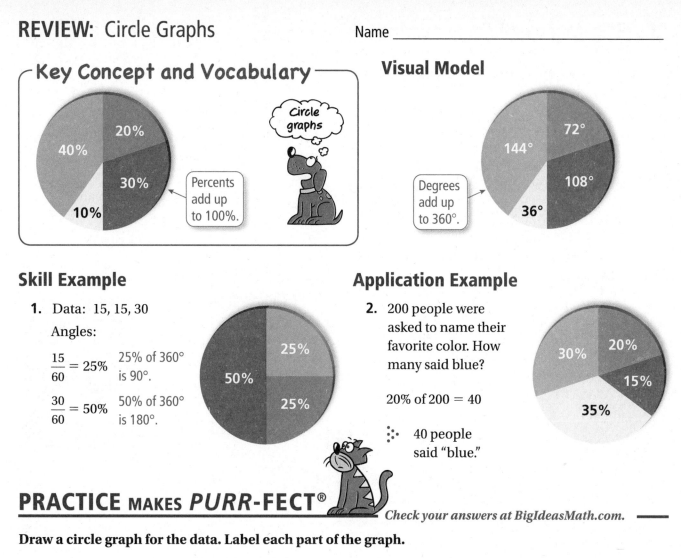

40% 20% 30% 10%

Percents add up to 100%.

Circle graphs

Visual Model

72° 144° 108° 36°

Degrees add up to 360°.

Skill Example

1. Data: 15, 15, 30

   Angles:

   $\frac{15}{60} = 25\%$ 25% of 360° is 90°.

   $\frac{30}{60} = 50\%$ 50% of 360° is 180°.

25% 50% 25% 25%

Application Example

2. 200 people were asked to name their favorite color. How many said blue?

   20% of 200 = 40

   ∴ 40 people said "blue."

30% 20% 15% 35%

PRACTICE MAKES *PURR*-FECT®

Check your answers at BigIdeasMath.com. ——

Draw a circle graph for the data. Label each part of the graph.

3. Favorite Pet:
   dog 9, cat 5,
   fish 3, bird 1

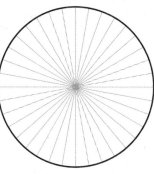

4. Favorite Day:
   Friday 9,
   Saturday 12,
   Sunday 15

BUDGET   A family is making a monthly budget. The total take-home pay for a month is $2400.

5. How much is budgeted for food? _____

6. How much is budgeted for miscellaneous? _____

7. How much is budgeted for rent? _____

8. How much is budgeted for clothes? _____

9. How much is budgeted for savings? _____

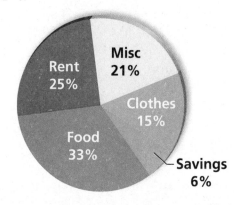

Misc 21%
Rent 25%
Clothes 15%
Food 33%
Savings 6%

REVIEW: Mean, Median, and Mode

Name _____

Key Concept and Vocabulary

mode = 1   median = 3.5

1, 1, 1, 3, 4, 5, 6, 7

$$\text{Mean} = \frac{1+1+1+3+4+5+6+7}{8}$$

$$= 3.5$$

Averages

Visual Model

Mean = 3.5

The scale balances at the mean.

Skill Example

1. mode = 1   median = 4

Outlier

1, 1, 1, 3, 4, 5, 6, 7, (17)

$$\text{Mean} = \frac{1+1+1+3+4+5+6+7+17}{9}$$

$$= 5$$

Application Example

2. What is the mean weight of the bowling balls?

$13 + 12 + 9 + 10 + 13 + 9 = 66$

$$\text{Mean} = \frac{66}{6} = 11$$

∴ The mean weight is 11 pounds.

13 lb   12 lb
9 lb   10 lb
13 lb   9 lb

PRACTICE MAKES *PURR-FECT*®

Check your answers at BigIdeasMath.com. ——

Find the mean, median, and mode of the data.

3. 2, 6, 9, 10, 3, 4, 6, 12, 4, 13

   Mean = ____, Median = ____, Mode = _____

4. 30, 48, 32, 43, 45, 32

   Mean = ____, Median = _____, Mode = _____

5. 18, 12, 25, 18, 17, 19, 29, 20, 13, 18

   Mean = _____, Median = ____, Mode = _____

6. 6.8, 6.2, 6.3, 6.8, 5.9, 6.0, 6.1, 5.9

   Mean = _____, Median = _____, Mode = _____

7. −4, 5, 3, −2, 1, 0, −2

   Mean = ____, Median = ____, Mode = _____

8. 2, 5, 5, 0, 12, 5, 7, 8, 12, 9

   Mean = ____, Median = ____, Mode = _____

9. **SALARIES** The weekly salaries of six employees at a fast-food restaurant are $140, $220, $90, $180, $140, and $200. Find the mean, median, and mode of these salaries.

   Mean = _____, Median = _____, Mode = _____

10. **PUPPIES** A litter of puppies is 8 weeks old. Find the mean, median, and mode of the weights of the puppies.

    5.1 lb   5.2 lb   5.4 lb   6.0 lb
    3.7 lb   5.5 lb   4.8 lb

    Mean = _____, Median = _____, Mode = _____

Name _____

Key Concept and Vocabulary

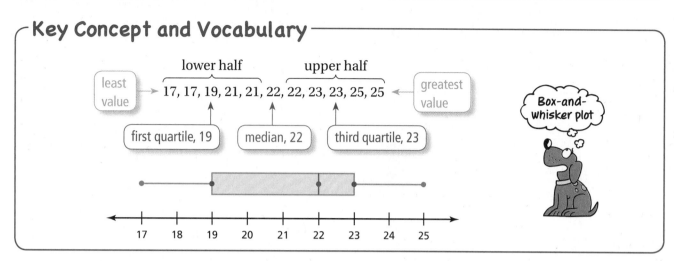

lower half   upper half

least value → 17, 17, 19, 21, 21, 22, 22, 23, 23, 25, 25 ← greatest value

first quartile, 19   median, 22   third quartile, 23

Box-and-whisker plot

17 18 19 20 21 22 23 24 25

Skill Example

1.

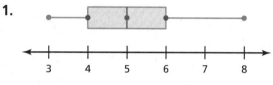

3   4   5   6   7   8

- The range of the data values is $8 - 3 = 5$.

- The interquartile range of the data values is $6 - 4 = 2$.

Application Example

2. Which store's prices are more spread out?

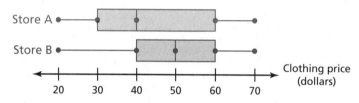

Store A

Store B

Clothing price (dollars)

20   30   40   50   60   70

The ranges are equal, but the interquartile range is greater for Store A.

∴ The prices in Store A are more spread out.

PRACTICE MAKES *PURR*-FECT®

Check your answers at BigIdeasMath.com.

Make a box-and-whisker plot for the data.

3. 12, 19, 16, 19, 14, 11, 11, 17, 14, 16, 18

4. 32, 28, 34, 35, 28, 32, 32, 30

11 12 13 14 15 16 17 18 19

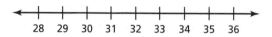

28 29 30 31 32 33 34 35 36

HEIGHT The double box-and-whisker plot shows the heights of students in two classrooms.

5. Which classroom's heights are more spread out? _____

6. Which classroom's students are generally taller? _____

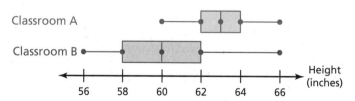

Classroom A

Classroom B

Height (inches)

56   58   60   62   64   66

REVIEW: Histograms

Name _____

Key Concept and Vocabulary

Data Value	Tally	Frequency
1	IIII	4
2	卌	5
3	III	3
4	III	3
5	II	2

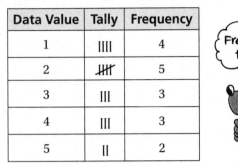

Frequency tables

Visual Model

A *histogram* shows the frequency of data values in intervals of the same size.

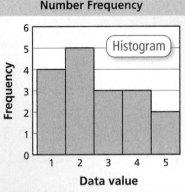

Number Frequency

Histogram

Skill Example

1. **Data:** 4, 6, 3, 6, 4, 5, 5, 6, 3, 5, 6, 3, 5, 6

Data Value	Tally	Frequency
3	III	3
4	II	2
5	IIII	4
6	卌	5

Application Example

2. How many 12-year-olds attended the swimming event?

∴ about 13

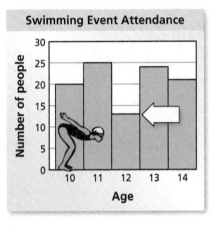

Swimming Event Attendance

PRACTICE MAKES *PURR-FECT*®

Check your answers at BigIdeasMath.com.

3. Make a frequency table for the data. Then draw a histogram for the data.

Ages

5, 5, 7, 8, 4, 7, 5,
6, 7, 8, 4, 6, 6, 5,
7, 7, 6, 6, 7, 4, 8,
4, 6, 6, 5, 5, 7, 6

Age	Tally	Frequency
4		
5		
6		
7		
8		

BIRTH WEIGHT The histogram shows the birth weights of babies at a hospital.

4. How many babies weigh 6 pounds? _____

5. How many weigh 7 pounds? _____

6. How many weigh less than 6 pounds? _____

7. How many weigh 6 or more pounds? _____

8. Approximate the mean birth weight. _____

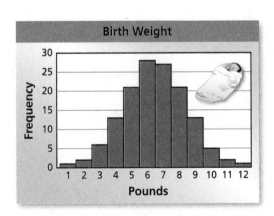

Birth Weight

Name _____

Key Concept and Vocabulary

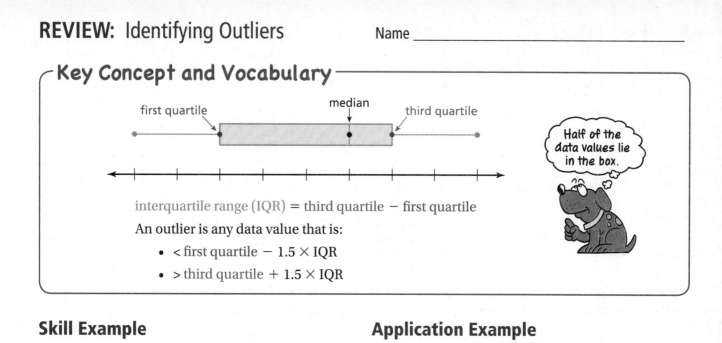

first quartile   median   third quartile

Half of the data values lie in the box.

interquartile range (IQR) = third quartile − first quartile

An outlier is any data value that is:
- < first quartile − 1.5 × IQR
- > third quartile + 1.5 × IQR

Skill Example

1.

$$\overbrace{10\ 21\ 21\ 23}^{\text{lower half}}\quad \overbrace{25\ 26\ 28\ 42}^{\text{upper half}}$$

first quartile, 21   third quartile, 27

IQR = 27 − 21 = 6

21 − 1.5 × 6 = 12   27 + 1.5 × 6 = 36

Because 10 < 12, 10 is an outlier.   Because 42 > 36, 42 is an outlier.

Application Example

2. The table shows the heights of seven students. Identify any outlier(s).

Height (inches)						
52	47	55	81	61	49	59

Order the data: 47, 49, 52, 55, 59, 61, 81

IQR = 61 − 49 = 12

49 − 1.5 × 12 = 31   61 + 1.5 × 12 = 79

Because 81 > 79, 81 is an outlier. There are no data values less than 31.

PRACTICE MAKES PURR-FECT®

Check your answers at BigIdeasMath.com.

Find the interquartile range.

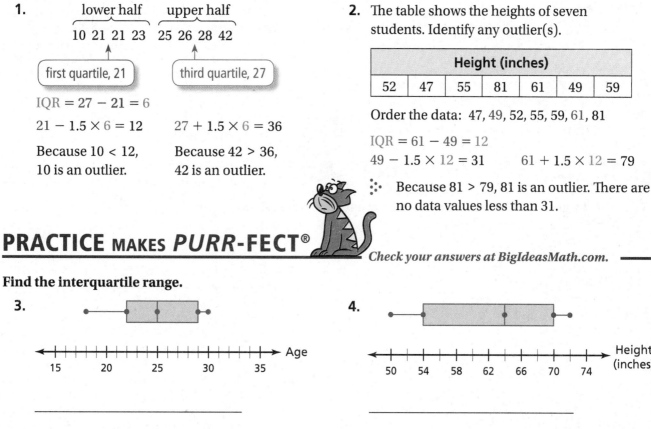

3.

                                    Age
    15   20   25   30   35

_____

4.

                                    Height (inches)
    50   54   58   62   66   70   74

_____

Identify any outlier(s) of the data set.

5. 8, 10, 13, 13, 14, 16, 27 _____

6. 20, 22, 22, 25, 28, 32, 34, 43 _____

7. 44, 51, 36, 19, 40, 69, 49, 46 _____

8. 76, 72, 64, 93, 80, 78, 96, 75, 70, 72 _____

9. **BASKETBALL** The table shows the free throw percentage of each player on a basketball team. Identify any outlier(s). _____

Free Throw Percentage			
75	72	54	69
82	51	74	76
79	85	75	84

Name _____

Key Concept and Vocabulary

Circle: 0 straight sides, 0 vertices

Triangle: 3 sides, 3 vertices

Quadrilateral: 4 sides, 4 vertices

Pentagon: 5 sides, 5 vertices

Hexagon: 6 sides, 6 vertices

Octagon: 8 sides, 8 vertices

Visual Models

Circle   Triangle   Quadrilateral

Pentagon   Hexagon   Octagon

Skill Example

1. The shape has 4 sides and 4 vertices. So, the shape is a quadrilateral.

Application Example

2. The drawing of the sun is made using one octagon and eight triangles.

PRACTICE MAKES *PURR-FECT*®

Check your answers at BigIdeasMath.com.

Write the number of sides and vertices. Then write the name of the shape.

3. _____ sides

    _____ vertices

    Shape: _____

4. _____ sides

    _____ vertices

    Shape: _____

5. **HOUSE** Draw a quadrilateral to make a house. Draw a triangle to make the roof, a quadrilateral to make the door, and a circle to make a window.

6. **HOUSE** Your friend draws the house and the roof in Exercise 5 using one shape. What shape does your friend use? _____

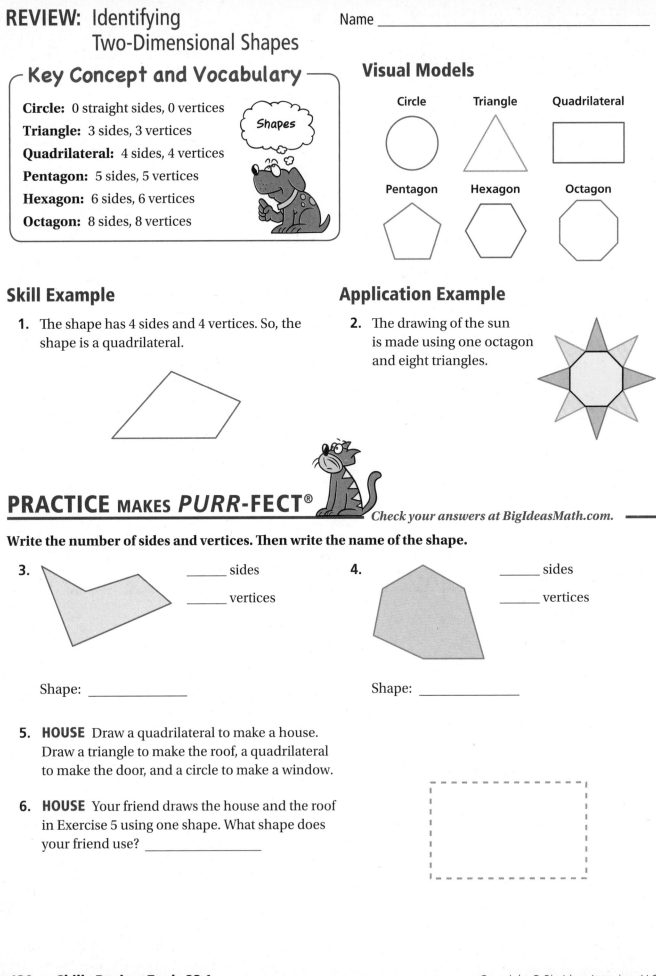

REVIEW: Classifying Triangles

Name _____

Key Concept and Vocabulary

Triangle	Diagram
A *right triangle* has one right angle.	
An *acute triangle* has three acute angles.	70° 50° 60°
An *obtuse triangle* has one obtuse angle.	40° 30° 110°
A *scalene triangle* has no sides with the same length.	
An *isosceles triangle* has two sides with the same length.	
An *equilateral triangle* has three sides with the same length.	
An *equiangular triangle* has three angles with the same measure.	

Classify.

Skill Example

1. The triangle has an obtuse angle and no sides with the same length. So, it is an obtuse scalene triangle.

5 ft   102°   4 ft

Application Example

2. The sides of the sign are the same length and the angles are the same measure.

∴ The sign is an equiangular equilateral triangle.

60° 60° 60°

PRACTICE MAKES *PURR*-FECT®

Check your answers at BigIdeasMath.com.

Classify the triangle by its angles and its sides.

3.
3 m 5 m 4 m

4.
8 in. 8 in. 8 in.

5.
48° 48° 84°

_____ _____ _____

REVIEW: Classifying Quadrilaterals

Name _____

Key Concept and Vocabulary

Quadrilateral	Diagram
A *trapezoid* has exactly 1 pair of parallel sides.	
A *parallelogram* has 2 pairs of parallel sides.	
A *rectangle* is a parallelogram with 4 right angles.	
A *rhombus* is a parallelogram with 4 congruent sides.	
A *square* is a parallelogram with 4 right angles and 4 congruent sides.	

Classify.

Visual Model

Quadrilaterals

trapezoids

parallelograms

rectangles

squares

rhombuses

Skill Examples

1. The quadrilateral has 4 right angles. Opposite sides have the same length, but all four sides are not the same length. So, the quadrilateral is a rectangle.

4 yd

2 yd   2 yd

4 yd

2. The quadrilateral has 0 right angles, 2 pairs of parallel sides, and four sides of the same length. So, the quadrilateral is a rhombus.

70°

110°   110°

70°

PRACTICE MAKES *PURR*-FECT®

Check your answers at BigIdeasMath.com.

Classify the quadrilateral in as many ways as possible.

3.

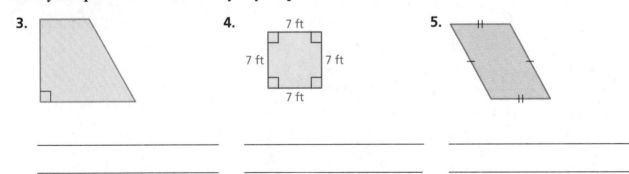

4.

7 ft

7 ft   7 ft

7 ft

5.

_____

_____

6. **RHOMBUS** A quadrilateral has 4 right angles. Is this enough information to determine whether the quadrilateral is a rhombus? Explain. _____

_____

Name _____

Key Concept and Vocabulary

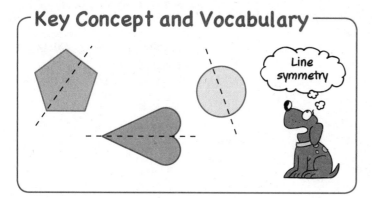

Line symmetry

Visual Model

If a figure has line symmetry, you can fold it on the line of symmetry so that two parts match exactly.

Skill Examples

1.

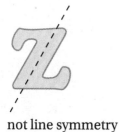

not line symmetry

2.

not line symmetry

Application Example

3. Is the house on the right identical to the house on the left?

∴ They are identical, but flipped over a vertical line of symmetry.

PRACTICE MAKES *PURR*-FECT®

Check your answers at BigIdeasMath.com.

Draw all lines of symmetry on the figure. If none, write "none."

4.

5.

6.

7.

8.

9.

10. **CLOWN** Which clown face has line symmetry? _____

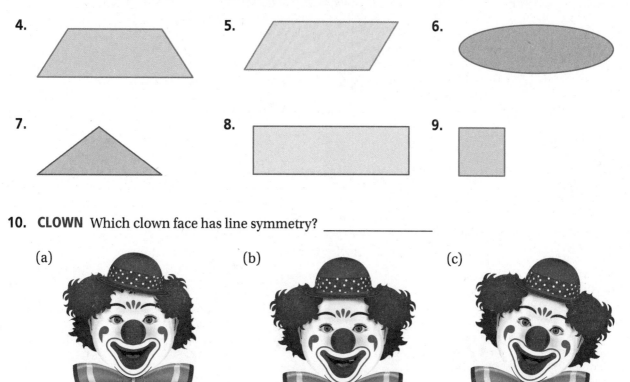

(a)

(b)

(c)

REVIEW: Rotational Symmetry

Name _____

Key Concept and Vocabulary

Rotational symmetry

Rotate about point *P*.

Visual Model

If a figure has rotational symmetry, you can rotate it about a point and the figure will coincide with itself.

(Rotate this worksheet 180°. The word will be the same.)

Skill Examples

1.

Rotational symmetry
120°, 240°

2.

Rotational symmetry
90°, 180°, 270°

Application Example

3. Why are traditional playing cards made with rotational symmetry?

⋮ When you rotate a playing card 180°, you see the same picture.

PRACTICE MAKES *PURR-FECT*®

Check your answers at BigIdeasMath.com.

List the angles (less than 360°) that represent rotational symmetry.

4. _____
       _____

5. _____
       _____

6. _____
       _____

7. _____
       _____

8. _____
       _____

9. _____
       _____

10. AMBIGRAM A rotational ambigram is a word that has rotational symmetry. Which of the following ambigrams contain the same word when rotated?

_____

(a)

(b) **WOW**

(c)

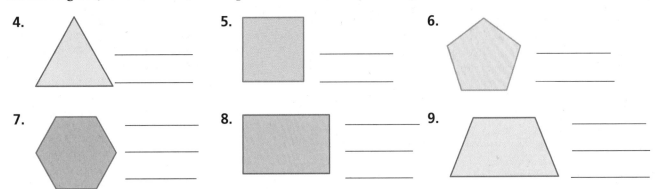

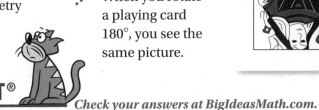

REVIEW: Using a Compass

Name _____

Key Concept and Vocabulary

Point

Pencil

Compass

Visual Model   Drawing a circle

Radius of circle

Center of circle

Skill Example

1. Copy the segment.

a.

A ●————————● B

C ●

cm 1 2 3 4 5 6 7 8 9 10

b.

A ●————————● B

C ●————————————

c.

A ●————————● B

C ●————————————● D

AB and *CD* have the same length.

PRACTICE MAKES *PURR-FECT*®

Check your answers at BigIdeasMath.com.

Use a straightedge and compass to copy the segment.

2. ●————————————●

3. ●————————————————————————————●

4. Draw a circle that has a radius of 3 centimeters.

5. Set the compass to a length of 1 inch. Complete the triangle so that it has sides of 4 inches, 3 inches, and 5 inches.

● Center of circle

Mark off a 4-inch line on this side.

Mark off a 3-inch line on this side.

REVIEW: Finding Perimeter Using Grids

Name _____

Key Concept and Vocabulary

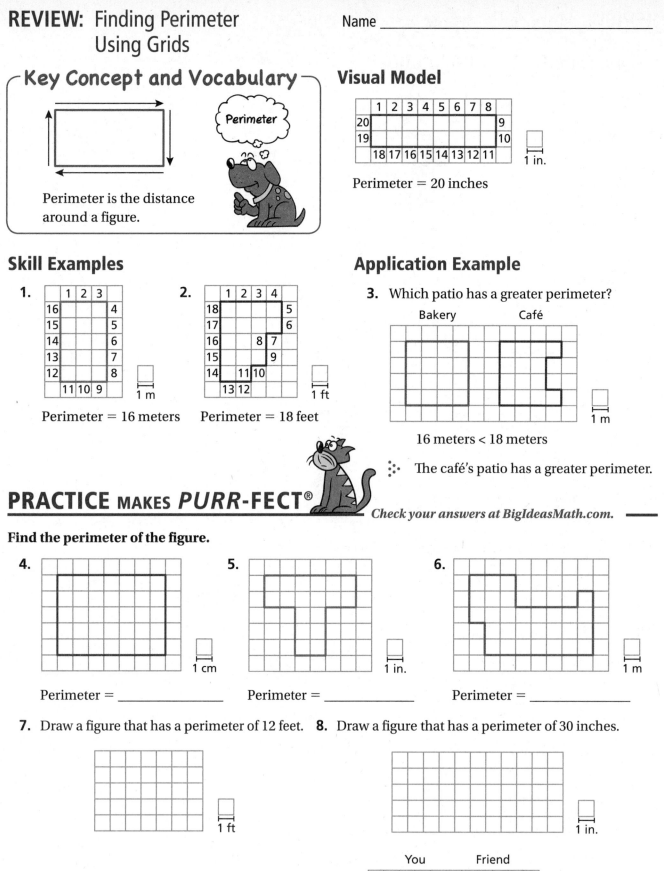

Perimeter is the distance around a figure.

Visual Model

Perimeter = 20 inches

Skill Examples

1.

Perimeter = 16 meters

2.

Perimeter = 18 feet

Application Example

3. Which patio has a greater perimeter?

Bakery   Café

16 meters < 18 meters

The café's patio has a greater perimeter.

PRACTICE MAKES *PURR-FECT*®

Check your answers at BigIdeasMath.com.

Find the perimeter of the figure.

4.

Perimeter = _____

5.

Perimeter = _____

6.

Perimeter = _____

7. Draw a figure that has a perimeter of 12 feet.

8. Draw a figure that has a perimeter of 30 inches.

9. GARDEN Whose garden has a greater perimeter?

_____

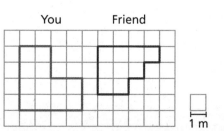

You   Friend

REVIEW: Finding Area Using Grids

Name _____

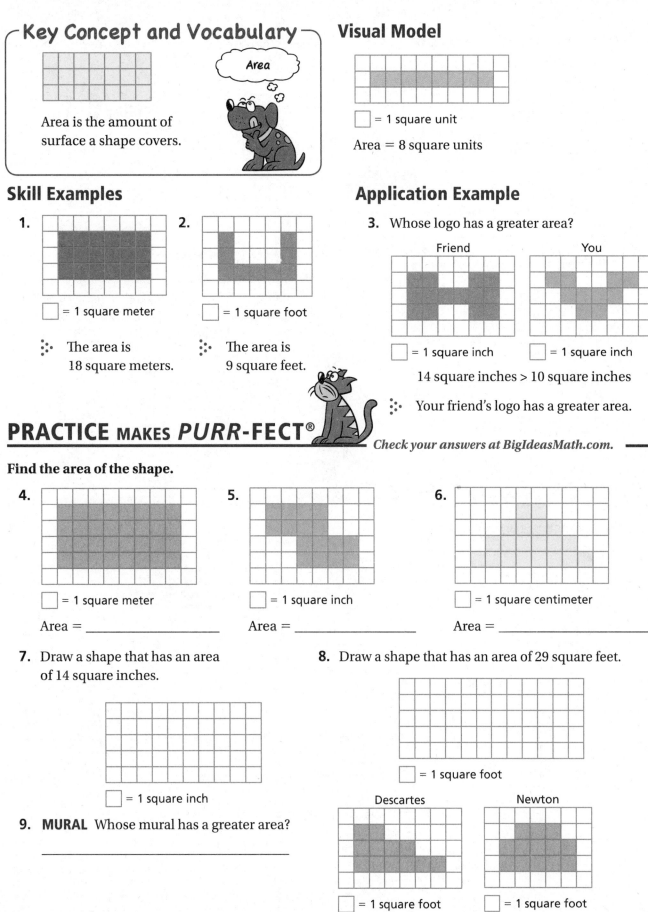

Key Concept and Vocabulary

Area is the amount of surface a shape covers.

Visual Model

☐ = 1 square unit

Area = 8 square units

Skill Examples

1. ☐ = 1 square meter

   ⋮ The area is 18 square meters.

2. ☐ = 1 square foot

   ⋮ The area is 9 square feet.

Application Example

3. Whose logo has a greater area?

   Friend

   You

   ☐ = 1 square inch   ☐ = 1 square inch

   14 square inches > 10 square inches

   ⋮ Your friend's logo has a greater area.

PRACTICE MAKES *PURR-FECT*®

Check your answers at BigIdeasMath.com.

Find the area of the shape.

4. ☐ = 1 square meter

   Area = _____

5. ☐ = 1 square inch

   Area = _____

6. ☐ = 1 square centimeter

   Area = _____

7. Draw a shape that has an area of 14 square inches.

   ☐ = 1 square inch

8. Draw a shape that has an area of 29 square feet.

   ☐ = 1 square foot

9. **MURAL** Whose mural has a greater area?

   _____

   Descartes

   Newton

   ☐ = 1 square foot   ☐ = 1 square foot

REVIEW: Formulas for Perimeter and Area of a Rectangle

Name _____

Key Concept and Vocabulary

Perimeter of a Rectangle

$P = (2 \times \ell) + (2 \times w)$

perimeter   length   width

Perimeter and area of a rectangle

Area of a Rectangle

$A = \ell \times w$

area   length   width

Visual Model

length = 8

width = 3

$P = (2 + \ell) + (2 + w)$ $A = \ell \times w$
$ = (2 \times 8) + (2 \times 3)$ $ = 8 \times 3$
$ = 16 + 6$ $ = 24$ square units
$ = 22$ units

Skill Examples

1.
16 cm

14 cm

$P = (2 \times 16) + (2 \times 14)$
$ = 32 + 28$
$ = 60$ centimeters

2.
9 ft

12 ft

$A = 12 \times 9$
$ = 108$ square feet

Application Example

3. You want to put string lights around a rectangular window that is 52 inches long and 32 inches wide. How many inches of lights do you need?

$P = (2 \times 52) + (2 \times 32)$
$ = 104 + 64$
$ = 168$ inches

You need 168 inches of lights.

PRACTICE MAKES *PURR*-FECT®

Check your answers at BigIdeasMath.com.

Find the perimeter of the rectangle.

4.
6 yd

7 yd

Perimeter = _____

5.
84 m

27 m

Perimeter = _____

6.
$3\frac{3}{4}$ cm

5 cm

Perimeter = _____

Find the area of the rectangle.

7.
9 in.

4 in.

Area = _____

8.
45 ft

38 ft

Area = _____

9.
$1\frac{1}{2}$ m

6 m

Area = _____

10. DIRT BIKE You ride a dirt bike around a rectangular track that is 154 meters long and 110 meters wide. How long is one lap around the track? _____

11. FLAG You design a rectangular flag that is 60 inches long and 36 inches wide. How many square inches of fabric do you need to make the flag? _____

REVIEW: Finding Perimeter

Name _____

Key Concept and Vocabulary

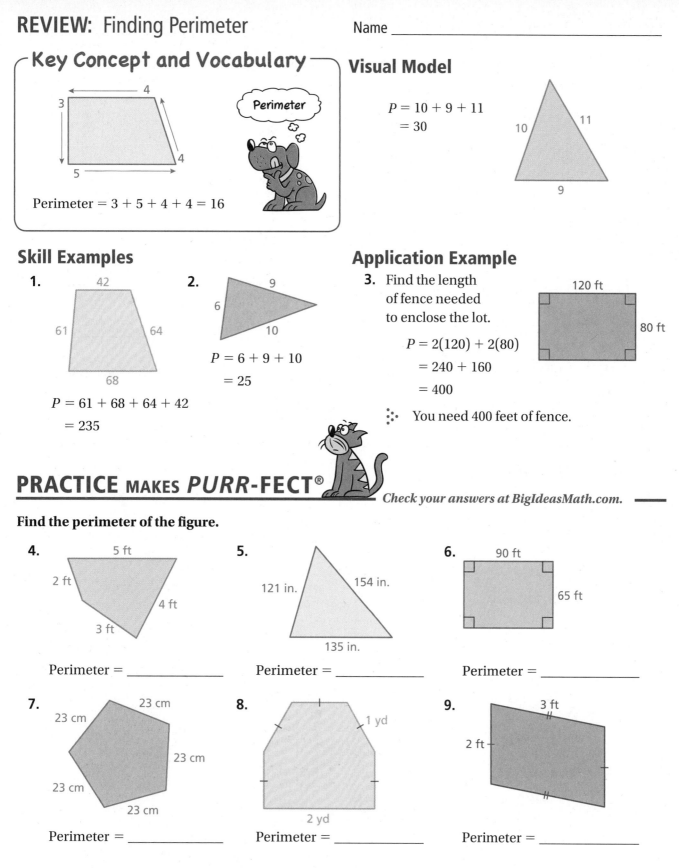

Perimeter = 3 + 5 + 4 + 4 = 16

Visual Model

$$P = 10 + 9 + 11$$
$$= 30$$

Skill Examples

1.

$$P = 61 + 68 + 64 + 42$$
$$= 235$$

2.

$$P = 6 + 9 + 10$$
$$= 25$$

Application Example

3. Find the length of fence needed to enclose the lot.

$$P = 2(120) + 2(80)$$
$$= 240 + 160$$
$$= 400$$

⁘ You need 400 feet of fence.

PRACTICE MAKES *PURR-FECT*®

Check your answers at BigIdeasMath.com.

Find the perimeter of the figure.

4.

Perimeter = _____

5.

Perimeter = _____

6.

Perimeter = _____

7.

Perimeter = _____

8.

Perimeter = _____

9.

Perimeter = _____

10. RIBBON You are wrapping a ribbon around a rectangular box that is 18 inches long and 12 inches wide. What is the minimum amount of ribbon you need? _____

11. COUNTY LINE A county has the shape of a quadrilateral. The lengths of the four sides are 109 miles, 94 miles, 82 miles, and 109 miles. Find the perimeter of the county. _____

REVIEW: Finding Area

Name _____

Key Concept and Vocabulary

Rectangle: $A = \ell w$

Parallelogram: $A = bh$

Triangle: $A = \frac{1}{2}bh$

Trapezoid: $A = \frac{1}{2}(b_1 + b_2)h$

Area formulas

Visual Model

Area of a Rectangle:

$A = \ell w$

$\quad = 12(10)$

$\quad = 120$ square units

width = 10

length = 12

Skill Examples

1.

1 cm

1 cm

1.2 cm

1.6 cm

$A = \frac{1}{2}(1.6 + 1)(1)$

$\quad = 1.3 \text{ cm}^2$

2.

2.4 in.

3.8 in.

$A = \frac{1}{2}(3.8)(2.4)$

$\quad = 4.56 \text{ in.}^2$

Application Example

3. Find the area of the rectangular apartment floor.

$A = 60 \cdot 40$

$\quad = 2400$

60 ft

40 ft

The area of the floor is 2400 square feet.

PRACTICE MAKES *PURR-FECT*®

Check your answers at BigIdeasMath.com.

Find the area of the figure.

4.

50 ft

30 ft

Area = _____

5.

10.6 in.

13.5 in.

Area = _____

6.

$\frac{1}{2}$ ft

$\frac{1}{4}$ ft

$\frac{3}{8}$ ft

Area = _____

7.

5 cm   6 cm

4 cm

5 cm

Area = _____

8.

8 yd

6 yd

2 yd

2 yd

Area = _____

9.

2 ft

$3\frac{1}{4}$ ft

Area = _____

10. CARPET You are carpeting a rectangular room that is 3.5 yards wide and 4.5 yards long. The carpet costs $15 per square yard. How much will it cost to carpet the room? _____

11. COLORADO Colorado is approximately a rectangle that is 280 miles wide and 380 miles long. Is the area of Colorado greater than or less than 100,000 square miles? Explain.

_____

REVIEW: Circles and Circumference

Name _____

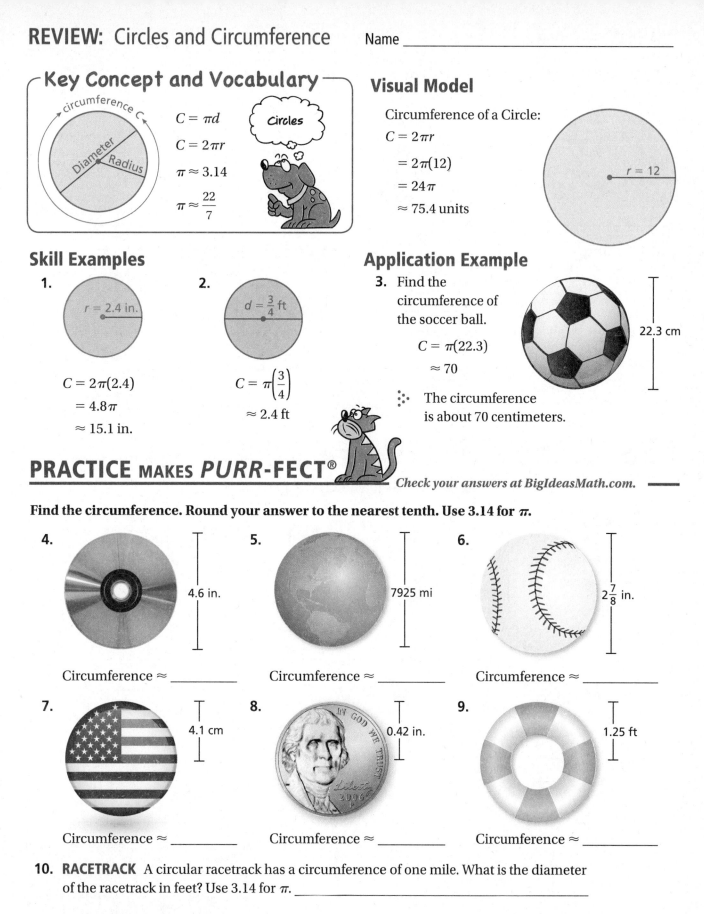

Key Concept and Vocabulary

circumference C

Diameter   Radius

$C = \pi d$

$C = 2\pi r$

$\pi \approx 3.14$

$\pi \approx \dfrac{22}{7}$

Circles

Visual Model

Circumference of a Circle:

$C = 2\pi r$

$\quad = 2\pi(12)$

$\quad = 24\pi$

$\quad \approx 75.4 \text{ units}$

$r = 12$

Skill Examples

1.

$r = 2.4$ in.

$C = 2\pi(2.4)$

$\quad = 4.8\pi$

$\quad \approx 15.1$ in.

2.

$d = \dfrac{3}{4}$ ft

$C = \pi\left(\dfrac{3}{4}\right)$

$\quad \approx 2.4$ ft

Application Example

3. Find the circumference of the soccer ball.

$C = \pi(22.3)$

$\quad \approx 70$

22.3 cm

The circumference is about 70 centimeters.

PRACTICE MAKES *PURR-FECT*®

Check your answers at BigIdeasMath.com.

Find the circumference. Round your answer to the nearest tenth. Use 3.14 for π.

4.

4.6 in.

Circumference ≈ _____

5.

7925 mi

Circumference ≈ _____

6.

$2\dfrac{7}{8}$ in.

Circumference ≈ _____

7.

4.1 cm

Circumference ≈ _____

8.

0.42 in.

Circumference ≈ _____

9.

1.25 ft

Circumference ≈ _____

10. RACETRACK A circular racetrack has a circumference of one mile. What is the diameter of the racetrack in feet? Use 3.14 for π. _____

11. OLD OAK TREE You have 110 inches of yellow ribbon. The diameter of an oak tree is 38 inches. Do you have enough yellow ribbon to wrap around the oak tree? Explain. Use 3.14 for π.

_____

REVIEW: Areas of Circles

Name _____

Key Concept and Vocabulary

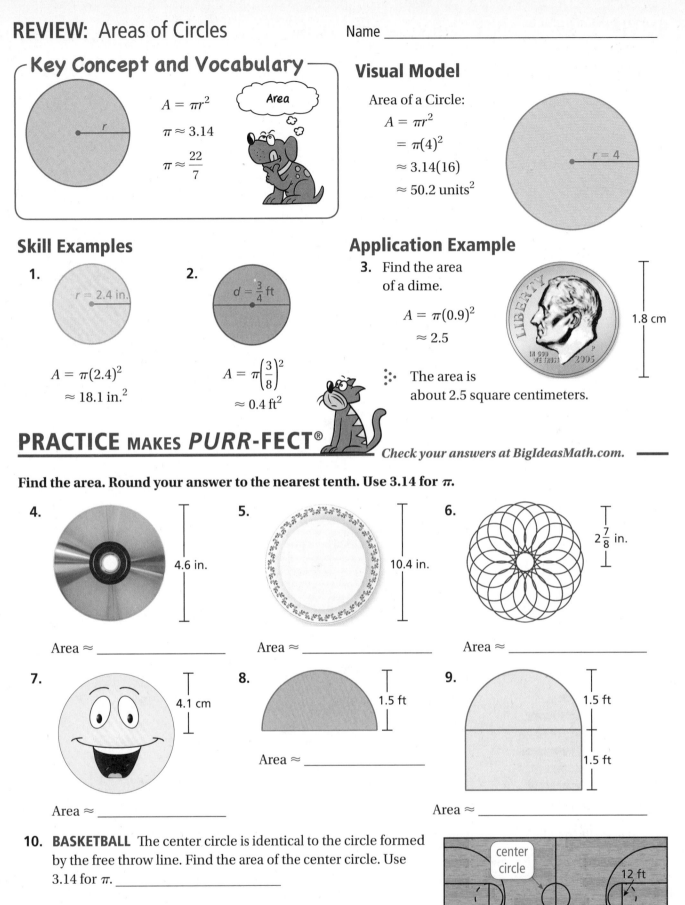

$A = \pi r^2$

$\pi \approx 3.14$

$\pi \approx \dfrac{22}{7}$

Area

Visual Model

Area of a Circle:

$A = \pi r^2$

$= \pi(4)^2$

$\approx 3.14(16)$

$\approx 50.2 \text{ units}^2$

$r = 4$

Skill Examples

1.

$r = 2.4$ in.

$A = \pi(2.4)^2$

$\approx 18.1 \text{ in.}^2$

2.

$d = \dfrac{3}{4}$ ft

$A = \pi\left(\dfrac{3}{8}\right)^2$

$\approx 0.4 \text{ ft}^2$

Application Example

3. Find the area of a dime.

$A = \pi(0.9)^2$

≈ 2.5

1.8 cm

⋮ The area is about 2.5 square centimeters.

PRACTICE MAKES *PURR*-FECT®

Check your answers at BigIdeasMath.com. ▬

Find the area. Round your answer to the nearest tenth. Use 3.14 for π.

4.

4.6 in.

Area ≈ _____

5.

10.4 in.

Area ≈ _____

6.

$2\dfrac{7}{8}$ in.

Area ≈ _____

7.

4.1 cm

Area ≈ _____

8.

1.5 ft

Area ≈ _____

9.

1.5 ft

1.5 ft

Area ≈ _____

10. **BASKETBALL** The center circle is identical to the circle formed by the free throw line. Find the area of the center circle. Use 3.14 for π. _____

11. **BASKETBALL** Find the area of the semicircular free throw region on the basketball court. Use 3.14 for π.

_____

center circle

12 ft

free throw

REVIEW: Points, Lines, and Rays

Name _____

Key Concept and Vocabulary

Definition	Example
A *point* is an exact location in space.	A •
A *line* is a straight path of points that goes on without end in both directions.	C ←———D→
A *line segment* is a part of a line that includes two endpoints and all of the points between them.	F———G
A *ray* is a part of a line that has one endpoint and goes on without end in one direction.	P———Q→

Points, lines, and rays

Skill Examples

1. J ←———• K →

    J and *K* lie on the line.
    So, the name of the line is $\overleftrightarrow{JK}$ or $\overleftrightarrow{KJ}$.

2. W •———• X

    The ray starts at *W* and passes through *X*.
    So, the name of the ray is $\overrightarrow{WX}$.

Application Example

3. The arrow on the sign has one endpoint and goes on without end in one direction.

    ∴ The arrow looks like a ray.

PRACTICE MAKES *PURR*-FECT®

Check your answers at BigIdeasMath.com. ——

Name the figure shown.

4. E
      \
       • F

5. P •

6. ←• M ————• N

_____ _____ _____

Draw and label the figure.

7. $\overrightarrow{XY}$

8. $\overleftrightarrow{RS}$

9. $\overline{BC}$

10. **ROAD SIGNS** Which road sign(s) contain a figure that looks like a line?

Key Concept and Vocabulary

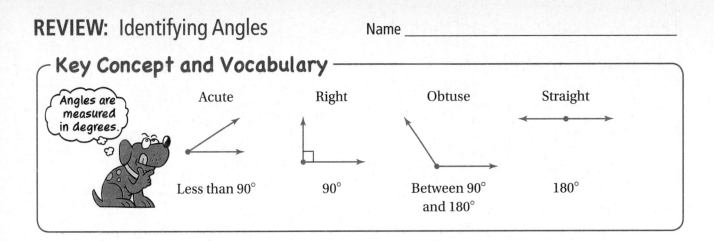

Angles are measured in degrees.

Acute	Right	Obtuse	Straight
Less than 90°	90°	Between 90° and 180°	180°

Skill Example

1.

Three names for the angle are ∠B, ∠ABC, and ∠CBA. The angle opens less than a right angle. So, it is an acute angle.

Application Example

2. Two obtuse angles in the flag of Brazil are ∠WXY and ∠YZW. Two acute angles are ∠ZWX and ∠XYZ.

PRACTICE MAKES *PURR*-FECT®

Check your answers at BigIdeasMath.com.

Write a name for the angle and classify it.

3.

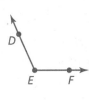

_____

4.

_____

5.   R   S   T

_____

Draw and label the angle.

6. ∠PQR is acute.

7. ∠JKL is right.

8. ∠TUV is obtuse.

9. **BILLIARDS** Classify the three angles of the triangle.

_____

REVIEW: Using a Protractor

Name _____

Key Concept and Vocabulary

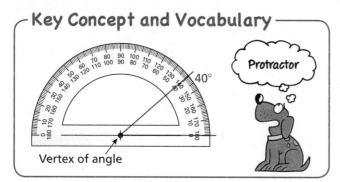

Vertex of angle

Protractor

Visual Model

Protractors have 2 sets of numbers in opposite directions. When in doubt as to which to use, think, *"Should this angle be greater than or less than 90°?"*

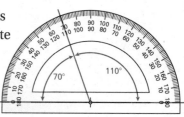

Skill Example

1. Measure an angle of the triangle.

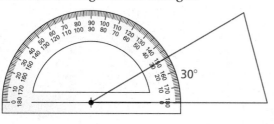

30°

Application Example

2. Measure the pitch angle of the roof.

Pitch angle

Pitch angle

⋮⋮ The angle is about 20°.

PRACTICE MAKES *PURR-FECT*®

Check your answers at BigIdeasMath.com.

Find the measure of the angle.

3.

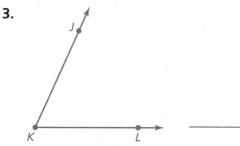

J

K   L

_____

4.

R

S   T

_____

Use a protractor to draw the angle.

5. 35°

6. 60°

7. 113°

8. **WINDOW** Measure each angle of the triangle.

A = _____

B = _____

C = _____

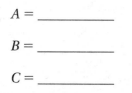

A

C   B

REVIEW: Using Angle Relationships

Name _____

Key Concept and Vocabulary

- The measures of two complementary angles add to 90°.
- The measures of two supplementary angles add to 180°.

Visual Model

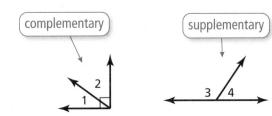

complementary · supplementary

Skill Examples

1.
49°
41°

$41° + 49° = 90°$
complementary

2.
70° 110°

$70° + 110° = 180°$
supplementary

Application Example

3. Find the measures of angles 1, 2, and 3.

$\angle 1 = 130°$
$\angle 2 = 50°$
$\angle 3 = 130°$

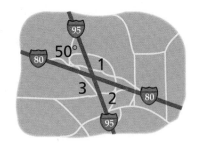

PRACTICE MAKES PURR-FECT®

Check your answers at BigIdeasMath.com.

Decide whether the angles are *complementary, supplementary,* or *neither.*

4.
42°
48°

_____

5.
45°
55°

_____

6.
59° 31°

_____

7.
115° 65°

_____

8.
156°
24°

_____

9.
122° 68°

_____

Find the value of *x.*

10.
$x°$
35°

_____

11.
$x°$
128°

_____

12.
117° $x°$

_____

13. **TRIBUTARY** A tributary joins a river at an angle of $x°$. Find the value of *x.* _____

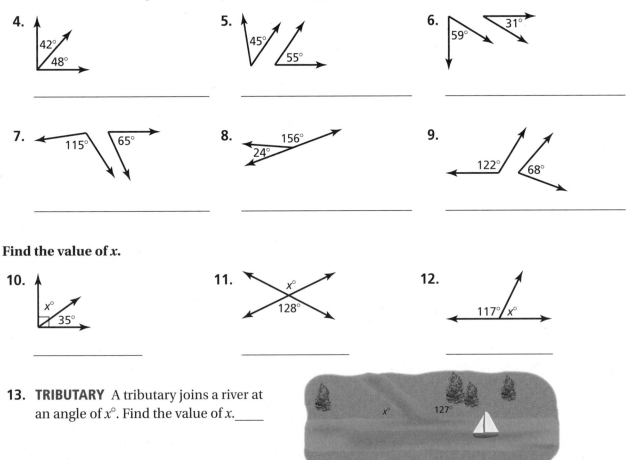

$x°$ 127°

REVIEW: Angles of Triangles

Name _____

Key Concept and Vocabulary

- The sum of the interior angle measures of a triangle is 180°.
- The measures of an exterior angle of a triangle is equal to the sum of the measures of the two nonadjacent interior angles.

Angles

Visual Model

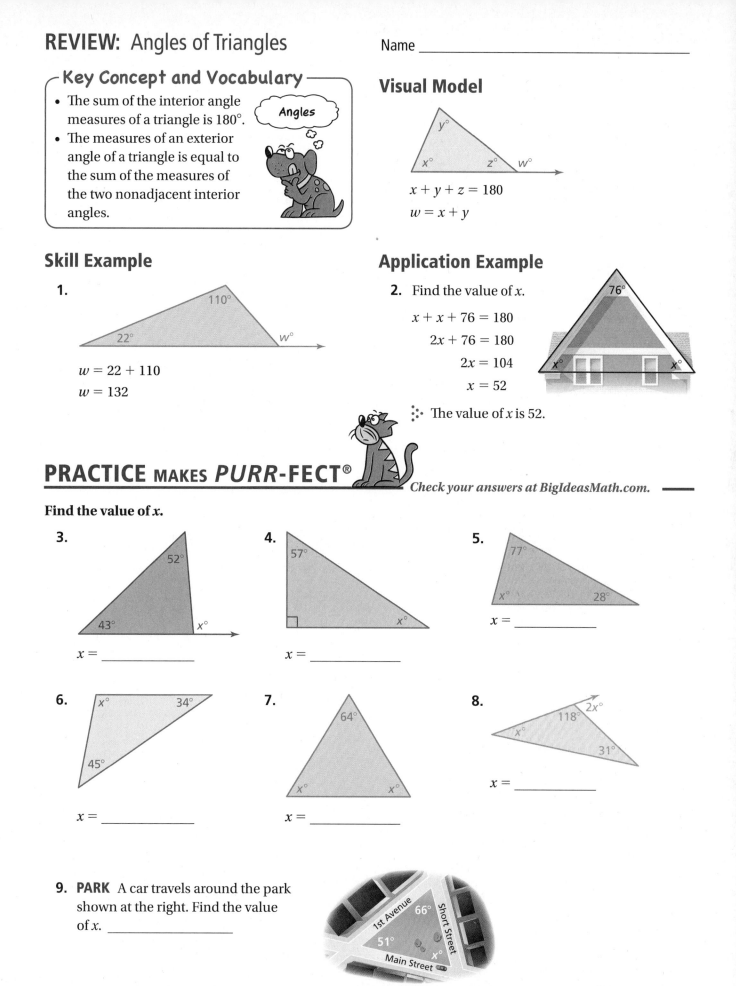

$x + y + z = 180$

$w = x + y$

Skill Example

1.

$w = 22 + 110$

$w = 132$

Application Example

2. Find the value of x.

$x + x + 76 = 180$

$2x + 76 = 180$

$2x = 104$

$x = 52$

⋮⋅ The value of x is 52.

PRACTICE MAKES *PURR*-FECT®

Check your answers at BigIdeasMath.com.

Find the value of x.

3.

$x =$ _____

4.

$x =$ _____

5.

$x =$ _____

6.

$x =$ _____

7.

$x =$ _____

8.

$x =$ _____

9. **PARK** A car travels around the park shown at the right. Find the value of x. _____

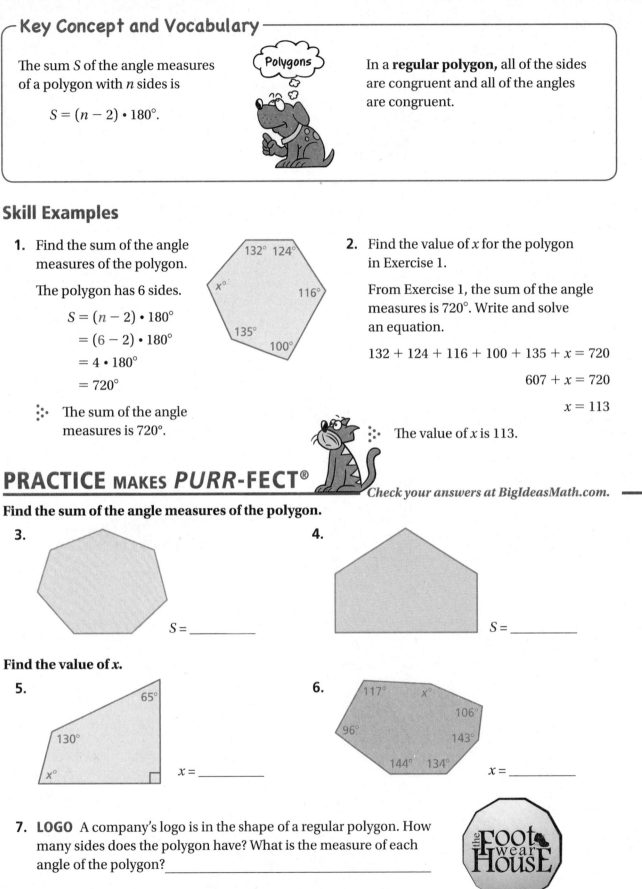

Key Concept and Vocabulary

The sum S of the angle measures of a polygon with n sides is

$$S = (n - 2) \cdot 180°.$$

Polygons

In a **regular polygon,** all of the sides are congruent and all of the angles are congruent.

Skill Examples

1. Find the sum of the angle measures of the polygon.

    The polygon has 6 sides.

    $$S = (n - 2) \cdot 180°$$
    $$= (6 - 2) \cdot 180°$$
    $$= 4 \cdot 180°$$
    $$= 720°$$

    The sum of the angle measures is 720°.

    132° 124°
    $x°$
    116°
    135°
    100°

2. Find the value of x for the polygon in Exercise 1.

    From Exercise 1, the sum of the angle measures is 720°. Write and solve an equation.

    $$132 + 124 + 116 + 100 + 135 + x = 720$$
    $$607 + x = 720$$
    $$x = 113$$

    The value of x is 113.

PRACTICE MAKES *PURR*-FECT®

Check your answers at BigIdeasMath.com.

Find the sum of the angle measures of the polygon.

3.

$S = $ _____

4.

$S = $ _____

Find the value of x.

5.

65°
130°
$x°$

$x = $ _____

6.

117° $x°$
106°
96°
143°
144° 134°

$x = $ _____

7. **LOGO** A company's logo is in the shape of a regular polygon. How many sides does the polygon have? What is the measure of each angle of the polygon? _____

    the Foot wear HOUSE

REVIEW: Parallel and Perpendicular Lines

Name _____

Skill Examples

1. $\overleftrightarrow{AB}$ and $\overleftrightarrow{CD}$ do not appear to intersect.

   ∴ So, $\overleftrightarrow{AB}$ and $\overleftrightarrow{CD}$ appear to be parallel lines.

2. $\overleftrightarrow{AD}$ and $\overleftrightarrow{CD}$ intersect to form four right angles.

   ∴ So, $\overleftrightarrow{AD}$ and $\overleftrightarrow{CD}$ are perpendicular lines.

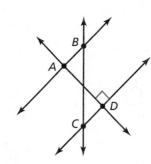

PRACTICE MAKES *PURR*-FECT®

Check your answers at BigIdeasMath.com.

Draw and label the lines with the given description.

3. $\overleftrightarrow{PQ} \perp \overleftrightarrow{RS}$

   $\overleftrightarrow{PQ}$ and $\overleftrightarrow{RS}$ intersect at point T.

4. $\overleftrightarrow{DE} \parallel \overleftrightarrow{FG}$

5. **INTERSECTION** Draw a road that appears to be perpendicular to Main Street and parallel to Broad Street.

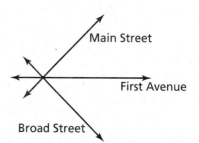

REVIEW: Parallel Lines and Transversals

Name _____

Key Concept and Vocabulary

A line that intersects two or more lines is called a **transversal.**

When a transversal intersects parallel lines, corresponding angles are congruent. Corresponding angles lie on the same side of the transversal in corresponding positions.

When a transversal intersects parallel lines, alternate interior angles are congruent and alternate exterior angles are congruent.

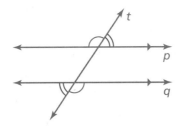

Corresponding angles

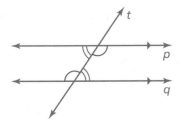

Alternate interior angles

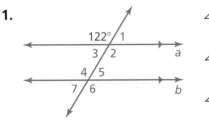

Alternate exterior angles

Skill Example

1.

∠6: ∠6 and the 122° angle are alternate exterior angles.
They are congruent. So, the measure of ∠6 is 122°.

∠3: ∠3 and the 122° angle are supplementary angles.
So, the measure of ∠3 is 180° − 122° = 58°.

∠5: ∠5 and ∠3 are alternate interior angles.
They are congruent. So, the measure of ∠5 is 58°.

∠1, ∠2, ∠4, and ∠7: Using corresponding angles, the measures of ∠1 and ∠7 are 58°, and the measures of ∠2 and ∠4 are 122°.

PRACTICE MAKES PURR-FECT®

Check your answers at BigIdeasMath.com.

Use the given angle to find the measures of the numbered angles. Explain your reasoning.

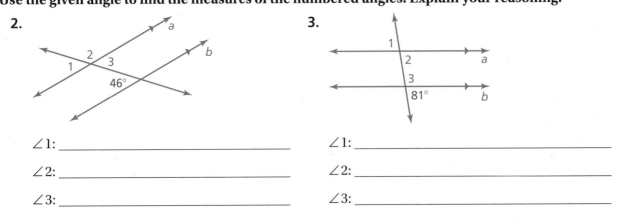

2.

∠1: _____

∠2: _____

∠3: _____

3.

∠1: _____

∠2: _____

∠3: _____

Key Concept and Vocabulary

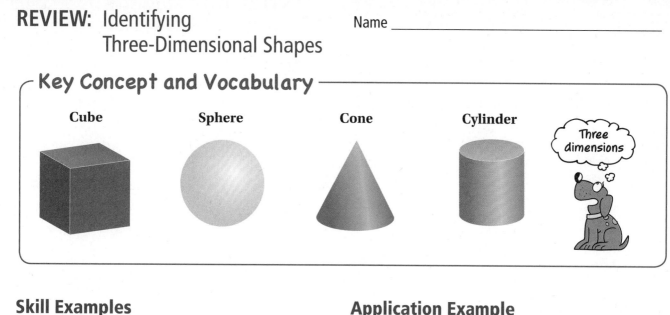

Cube   **Sphere**   **Cone**   **Cylinder**

Three dimensions

Skill Examples

1.   The shape has a curved surface and no flat surfaces.

⠿   So, the shape is a sphere.

2.   The shape has a curved surface and one flat surfaces.

⠿   So, the shape is a cone.

Application Example

3.   The glue stick has a curved surface and two flat surfaces.

⠿   So, the glue stick is a cylinder.

Glue stick

PRACTICE MAKES *PURR*-FECT®

Check your answers at BigIdeasMath.com.

Write the name of the shape.

4.

5.

6.

_____   _____   _____

7.   CRATE Draw the shape of the flat surfaces of the cube. Count and write the number of flat surfaces.

_____ flat surfaces

REVIEW: Faces, Edges, and Vertices

Name _____

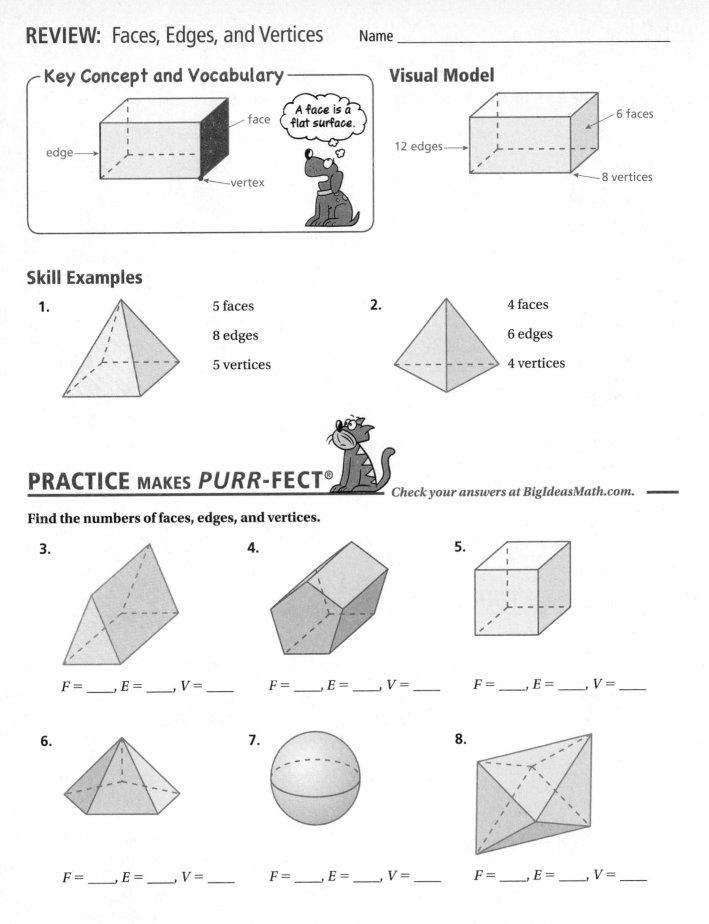

Key Concept and Vocabulary

edge →

face

A face is a flat surface.

→ vertex

Visual Model

12 edges →

6 faces

8 vertices

Skill Examples

1.

5 faces

8 edges

5 vertices

2.

4 faces

6 edges

4 vertices

PRACTICE MAKES *PURR-FECT*®

Check your answers at BigIdeasMath.com.

Find the numbers of faces, edges, and vertices.

3.

$F =$ ____, $E =$ ____, $V =$ ____

4.

$F =$ ____, $E =$ ____, $V =$ ____

5.

$F =$ ____, $E =$ ____, $V =$ ____

6.

$F =$ ____, $E =$ ____, $V =$ ____

7.

$F =$ ____, $E =$ ____, $V =$ ____

8.

$F =$ ____, $E =$ ____, $V =$ ____

9. **NUMBER CUBE** You roll a number cube. How many faces, edges, and vertices does the number cube have? _____

REVIEW: Surface Areas of Prisms

Name _____

Key Concept and Vocabulary

Surface Area of a Rectangular Prism

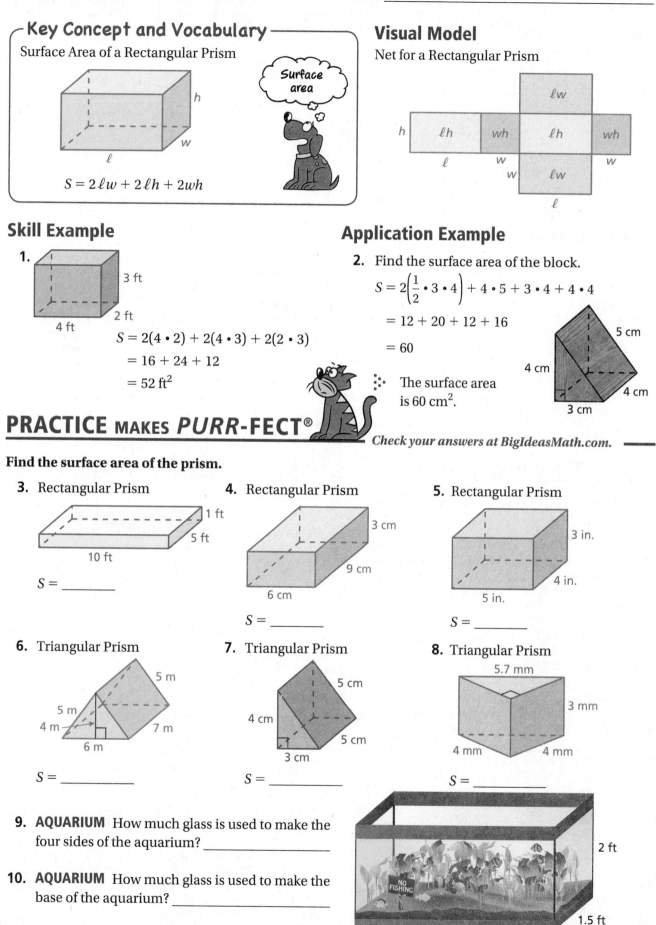

$S = 2\ell w + 2\ell h + 2wh$

Visual Model

Net for a Rectangular Prism

Skill Example

1.

3 ft
2 ft
4 ft

$S = 2(4 \cdot 2) + 2(4 \cdot 3) + 2(2 \cdot 3)$
$= 16 + 24 + 12$
$= 52 \text{ ft}^2$

Application Example

2. Find the surface area of the block.

$$S = 2\left(\frac{1}{2} \cdot 3 \cdot 4\right) + 4 \cdot 5 + 3 \cdot 4 + 4 \cdot 4$$
$$= 12 + 20 + 12 + 16$$
$$= 60$$

The surface area is 60 cm^2.

5 cm
4 cm
4 cm
3 cm

PRACTICE MAKES PURR-FECT®

Check your answers at BigIdeasMath.com.

Find the surface area of the prism.

3. Rectangular Prism

1 ft
5 ft
10 ft

$S = $ _____

4. Rectangular Prism

3 cm
9 cm
6 cm

$S = $ _____

5. Rectangular Prism

3 in.
4 in.
5 in.

$S = $ _____

6. Triangular Prism

5 m
5 m
4 m
7 m
6 m

$S = $ _____

7. Triangular Prism

5 cm
4 cm
5 cm
3 cm

$S = $ _____

8. Triangular Prism

5.7 mm
3 mm
4 mm
4 mm

$S = $ _____

9. AQUARIUM How much glass is used to make the four sides of the aquarium? _____

10. AQUARIUM How much glass is used to make the base of the aquarium? _____

2 ft
1.5 ft
4 ft

NO FISHING

REVIEW: Surface Areas of Cylinders

Name _____

Key Concept and Vocabulary

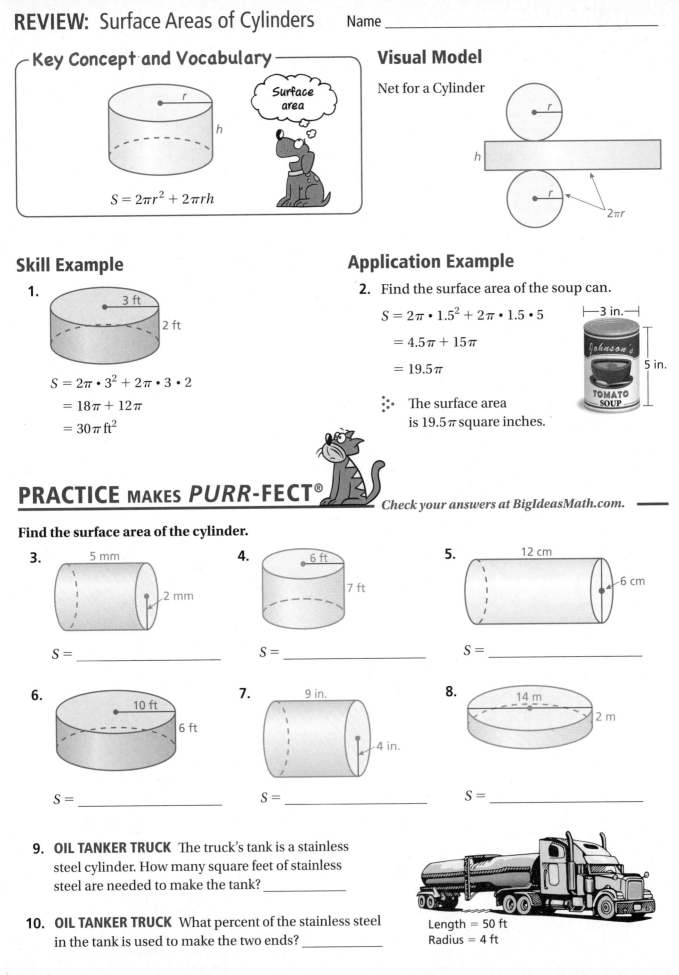

$$S = 2\pi r^2 + 2\pi rh$$

Surface area

Visual Model

Net for a Cylinder

$2\pi r$

Skill Example

1.

3 ft

2 ft

$$S = 2\pi \cdot 3^2 + 2\pi \cdot 3 \cdot 2$$
$$= 18\pi + 12\pi$$
$$= 30\pi \ \text{ft}^2$$

Application Example

2. Find the surface area of the soup can.

$$S = 2\pi \cdot 1.5^2 + 2\pi \cdot 1.5 \cdot 5$$
$$= 4.5\pi + 15\pi$$
$$= 19.5\pi$$

⋮⋅ The surface area
is 19.5π square inches.

3 in.

Johnson's

5 in.

TOMATO SOUP

PRACTICE MAKES PURR-FECT®

Check your answers at BigIdeasMath.com.

Find the surface area of the cylinder.

3.　5 mm

2 mm

$S =$ _____

4.　6 ft

7 ft

$S =$ _____

5.　12 cm

6 cm

$S =$ _____

6.　10 ft

6 ft

$S =$ _____

7.　9 in.

4 in.

$S =$ _____

8.　14 m

2 m

$S =$ _____

9. **OIL TANKER TRUCK** The truck's tank is a stainless
steel cylinder. How many square feet of stainless
steel are needed to make the tank? _____

10. **OIL TANKER TRUCK** What percent of the stainless steel
in the tank is used to make the two ends? _____

Length = 50 ft
Radius = 4 ft

REVIEW: Surface Areas of Pyramids

Name _____

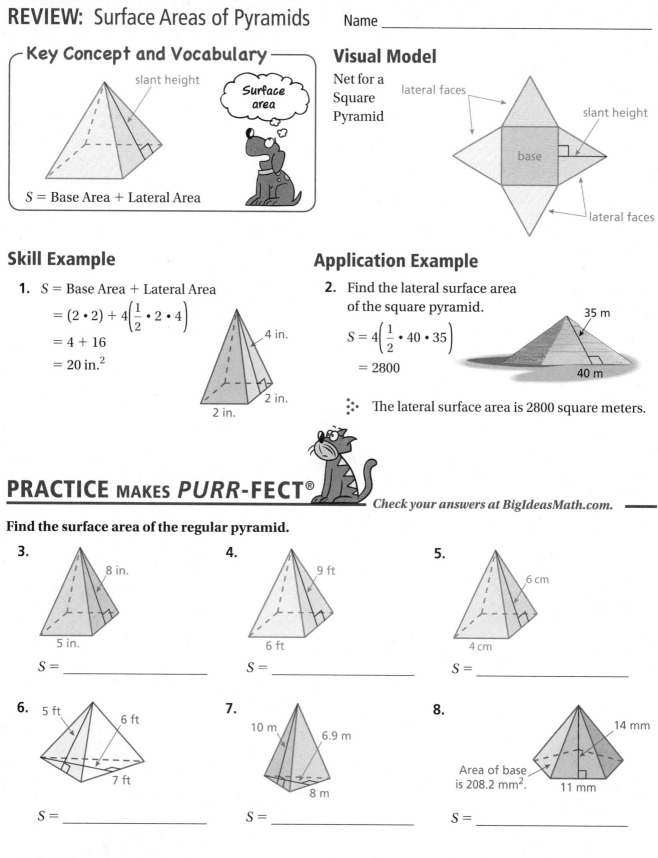

Key Concept and Vocabulary

slant height

Surface area

S = Base Area + Lateral Area

Visual Model

Net for a Square Pyramid

lateral faces

slant height

base

lateral faces

Skill Example

1. S = Base Area + Lateral Area

$= (2 \cdot 2) + 4\left(\dfrac{1}{2} \cdot 2 \cdot 4\right)$

$= 4 + 16$

$= 20 \text{ in.}^2$

4 in.

2 in.

2 in.

Application Example

2. Find the lateral surface area of the square pyramid.

$S = 4\left(\dfrac{1}{2} \cdot 40 \cdot 35\right)$

$= 2800$

35 m

40 m

The lateral surface area is 2800 square meters.

PRACTICE MAKES PURR-FECT®

Check your answers at BigIdeasMath.com.

Find the surface area of the regular pyramid.

3.

8 in.

5 in.

$S =$ _____

4.

9 ft

6 ft

$S =$ _____

5.

6 cm

4 cm

$S =$ _____

6.

5 ft   6 ft

7 ft

$S =$ _____

7.

10 m   6.9 m

8 m

$S =$ _____

8.

14 mm

Area of base is 208.2 mm².

11 mm

$S =$ _____

9. **ROOF** A roof in the shape of a square pyramid is covered with shingles. The roof has a slant height of 14 feet and a base with side lengths of 22 feet. The shingles cost $0.80 per square foot. How much does it cost to buy enough shingles to cover the roof? _____

REVIEW: Volumes of Rectangular Prisms

Name _____

Key Concept and Vocabulary

Area of base

Volume

$V = Bh$
$\quad = \ell \times w \times h$

Visual Model

$V = \ell \times w \times h$
$\quad = 2 \times 4 \times 3$
$\quad = 24 \text{ units}^3$

Skill Example

1.

3 ft
2 ft
5 ft

$S = 5 \times 2 \times 3$
$\quad = 30 \text{ ft}^3$

Application Example

2. An air mattress is 6 feet long, 4 feet wide, and 1 foot tall. What is the volume of the air mattress?

$V = \ell wh$
$\quad = 6 \times 4 \times 1$
$\quad = 24$

∴ The volume is 24 cubic feet.

PRACTICE MAKES PURR-FECT®

Check your answers at BigIdeasMath.com.

Find the volume of the rectangular prism.

3.

2 ft
2 ft
2 ft

$V = $ _____

4.

2 in.
2 in.
3 in.

$V = $ _____

5.

3 cm
4 cm
4 cm

$V = $ _____

6.

1 ft
5 ft
10 ft

$V = $ _____

7.

3 cm
9 cm
6 cm

$V = $ _____

8.

3 in.
4 in.
5 in.

$V = $ _____

9. **AQUARIUM** How much water is needed to fill the aquarium? _____

10. **AQUARIUM** There are about 7.5 gallons in 1 cubic foot. How many gallons of water does the aquarium hold? _____

2 ft
2 ft
4 ft

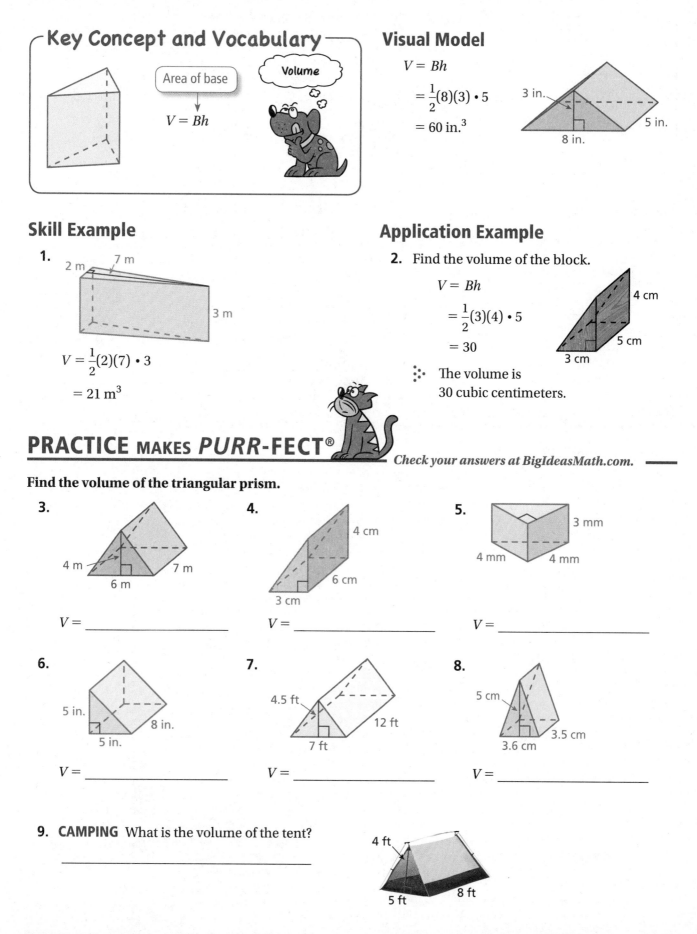

Key Concept and Vocabulary

Area of base

$V = Bh$

Volume

Visual Model

$V = Bh$

$= \dfrac{1}{2}(8)(3) \cdot 5$

$= 60 \text{ in.}^3$

3 in.

5 in.

8 in.

Skill Example

1.

2 m   7 m

3 m

$V = \dfrac{1}{2}(2)(7) \cdot 3$

$= 21 \text{ m}^3$

Application Example

2. Find the volume of the block.

$V = Bh$

$= \dfrac{1}{2}(3)(4) \cdot 5$

$= 30$

4 cm

5 cm

3 cm

The volume is
30 cubic centimeters.

PRACTICE MAKES *PURR-FECT*®

Check your answers at BigIdeasMath.com.

Find the volume of the triangular prism.

3.

4 m   7 m

6 m

$V =$ _____

4.

4 cm

6 cm

3 cm

$V =$ _____

5.

3 mm

4 mm   4 mm

$V =$ _____

6.

5 in.

8 in.

5 in.

$V =$ _____

7.

4.5 ft

12 ft

7 ft

$V =$ _____

8.

5 cm

3.5 cm

3.6 cm

$V =$ _____

9. CAMPING What is the volume of the tent?

_____

4 ft

5 ft   8 ft

REVIEW: Volumes of Cylinders

Name _____

Key Concept and Vocabulary

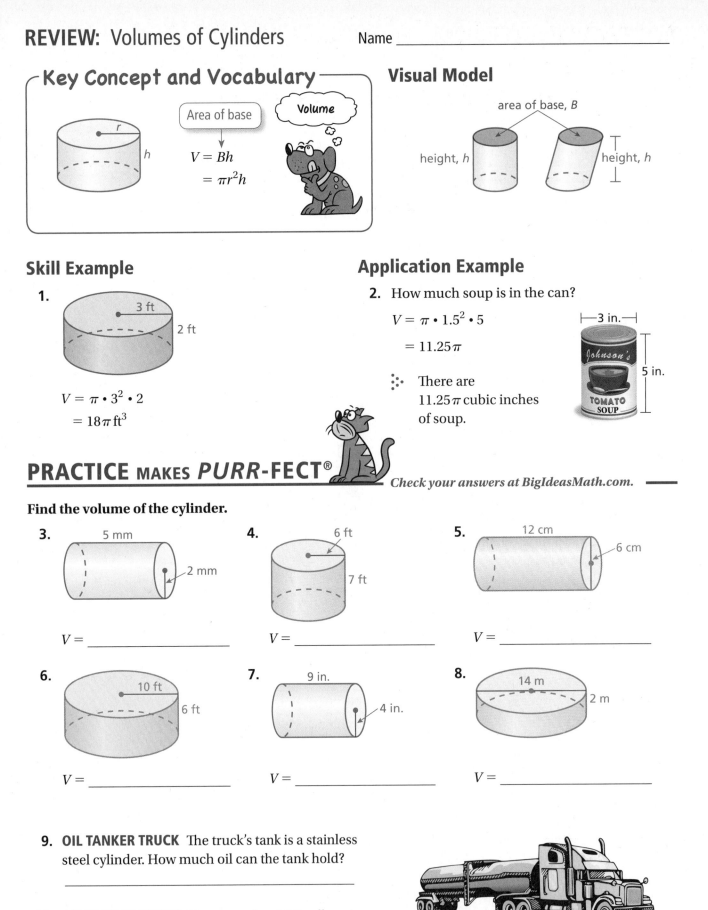

Area of base

Volume

$V = Bh$
$= \pi r^2 h$

Visual Model

area of base, B

height, h

height, h

Skill Example

1.

3 ft

2 ft

$V = \pi \cdot 3^2 \cdot 2$
$= 18\pi \text{ ft}^3$

Application Example

2. How much soup is in the can?

$V = \pi \cdot 1.5^2 \cdot 5$

$= 11.25\pi$

∴ There are
11.25π cubic inches
of soup.

├─ 3 in. ─┤

Johnson's

5 in.

TOMATO
SOUP

PRACTICE MAKES *PURR-FECT*®

Check your answers at BigIdeasMath.com.

Find the volume of the cylinder.

3.

5 mm

2 mm

$V = $ _____

4.

6 ft

7 ft

$V = $ _____

5.

12 cm

6 cm

$V = $ _____

6.

10 ft

6 ft

$V = $ _____

7.

9 in.

4 in.

$V = $ _____

8.

14 m

2 m

$V = $ _____

9. **OIL TANKER TRUCK** The truck's tank is a stainless
   steel cylinder. How much oil can the tank hold?

   _____

10. **OIL TANKER TRUCK** There are about 7.5 gallons in
    1 cubic foot. How many gallons of oil can the tank hold?

    _____

Length = 50 ft
Radius = 4 ft

REVIEW: Volumes of Pyramids

Name _____

Key Concept and Vocabulary

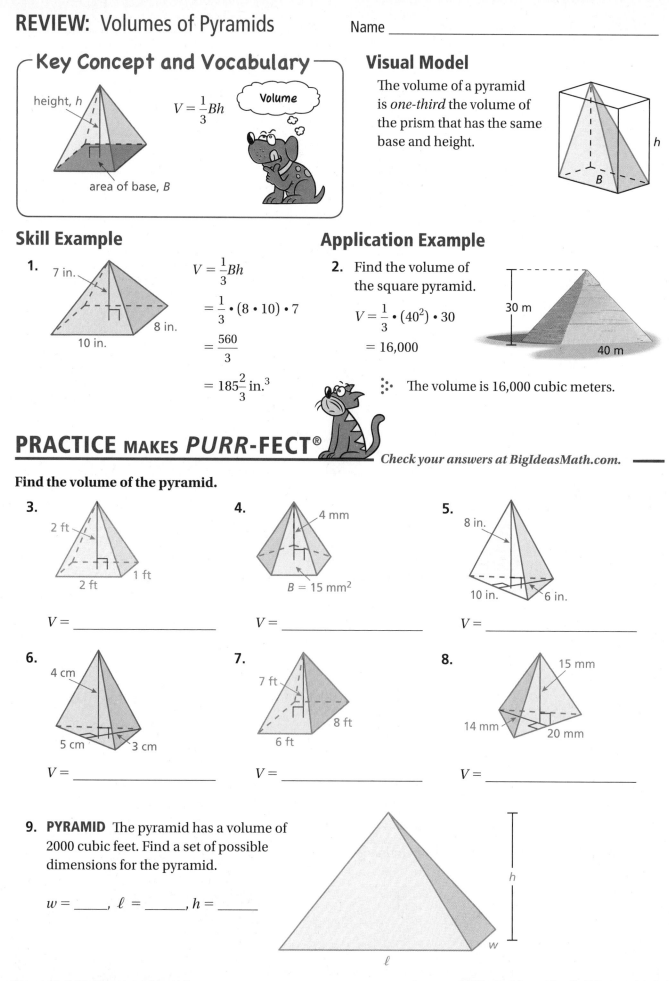

height, h

$V = \frac{1}{3}Bh$

Volume

area of base, B

Visual Model

The volume of a pyramid is *one-third* the volume of the prism that has the same base and height.

h

B

Skill Example

1. 7 in.

8 in.

10 in.

$V = \frac{1}{3}Bh$

$= \frac{1}{3} \cdot (8 \cdot 10) \cdot 7$

$= \frac{560}{3}$

$= 185\frac{2}{3}$ in.^{3}

Application Example

2. Find the volume of the square pyramid.

$V = \frac{1}{3} \cdot (40^2) \cdot 30$

$= 16,000$

30 m

40 m

The volume is 16,000 cubic meters.

PRACTICE MAKES *PURR-FECT*®

Check your answers at BigIdeasMath.com.

Find the volume of the pyramid.

3. 2 ft

2 ft   1 ft

$V = $ _____

4. 4 mm

$B = 15$ mm^2

$V = $ _____

5. 8 in.

10 in.   6 in.

$V = $ _____

6. 4 cm

5 cm   3 cm

$V = $ _____

7. 7 ft

6 ft   8 ft

$V = $ _____

8. 15 mm

14 mm   20 mm

$V = $ _____

9. **PYRAMID** The pyramid has a volume of 2000 cubic feet. Find a set of possible dimensions for the pyramid.

$w = $ _____, $\ell = $ _____, $h = $ _____

h

w

ℓ

Name _____

Key Concept and Vocabulary

height, h

area of base, B

Volume

$V = \frac{1}{3}Bh$

Visual Model

The volume of a cone is *one-third* the volume of the cylinder that has the same base and height.

h

B

Skill Example

1. 6 cm

    15 cm

    $V = \frac{1}{3}Bh$

    $= \frac{1}{3} \cdot (\pi \cdot 6^2) \cdot 15$

    $= 180\pi \text{ cm}^3$

Application Example

2. How much water can the funnel hold?

    $V = \frac{1}{3} \cdot (\pi \cdot 3^2) \cdot 5$

    $= 15\pi$

    ∵ It can hold 15π cubic inches.

    $r = 3$ in.

    $h = 5$ in.

PRACTICE MAKES *PURR-FECT*®

Check your answers at BigIdeasMath.com.

Find the volume of the cone.

3. 7 ft

    3 ft

    $V = $ _____

4. 4 in.

    2 in.

    $V = $ _____

5. 3 m

    6 m

    $V = $ _____

6. 2 ft   1 ft

    $V = $ _____

7. 10 mm

    5 mm

    $V = $ _____

8. 5 cm

    8 cm

    $V = $ _____

9. **LEMONADE** You have 10 gallons of lemonade (1 gal ≈ 3785 cm³). How many of the paper cups should you order? Explain. _____

    _____

    _____

    ⊢ 8 cm ⊣

    11 cm

REVIEW: Volumes of Spheres

Name _____

Key Concept and Vocabulary

radius, r

Volume

$$V = \frac{4}{3}\pi r^3$$

Visual Model

A hemisphere is one-half of a sphere.

hemispheres

Skill Example

1.

3 ft

$$V = \frac{4}{3}\pi \cdot 3^2$$
$$= 36\pi \text{ ft}^3$$

Application Example

2. Find the volume of the globe.

$$V = \frac{4}{3}\pi \cdot 9^3$$
$$= 972\pi$$

The volume is 972π cubic inches.

9 in.

PRACTICE MAKES *PURR-FECT*®

Check your answers at BigIdeasMath.com.

Find the volume of the sphere.

3.

6 in.

$V =$ _____

4.

10 m

$V =$ _____

5.

12 ft

$V =$ _____

6.

24 yd

$V =$ _____

7.

11 cm

$V =$ _____

8.

4 mm

$V =$ _____

9. **VOLLEYBALL** A box is in the shape of a cube with edge lengths of 8 inches. Will the volleyball fit inside the box? _____

Volume = 320 in.³

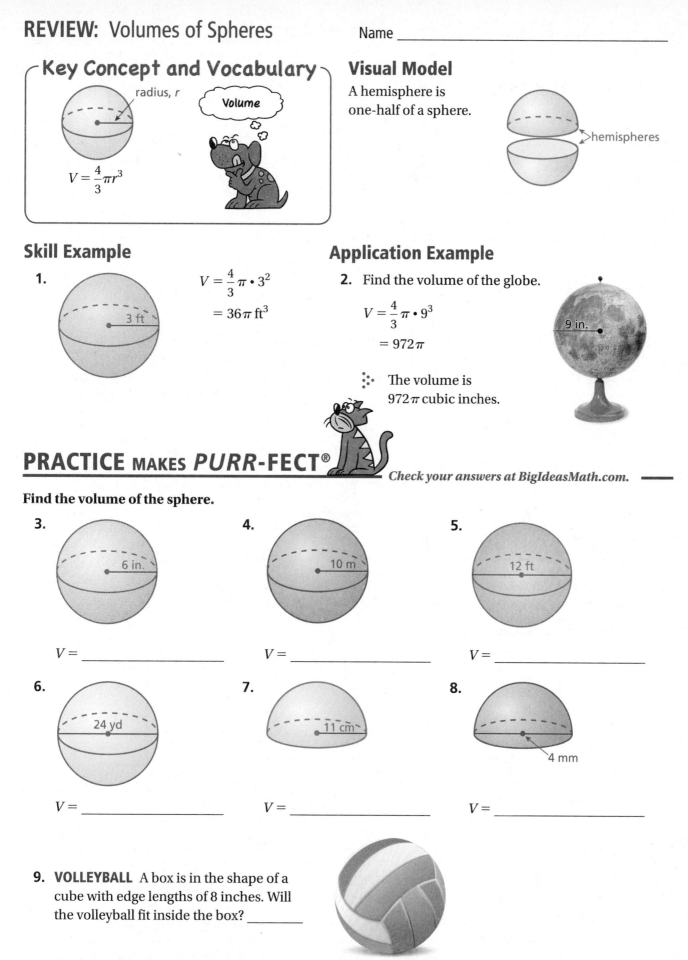

REVIEW: Translations

Name _____

Key Concept and Vocabulary

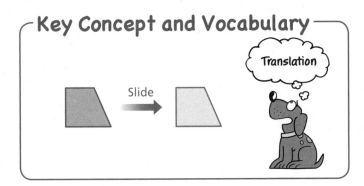

Slide

Translation

Visual Model

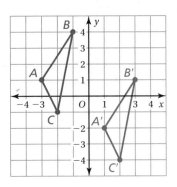

Every point of
the figure moves
the same distance
and in the same
direction.

Skill Example

1.

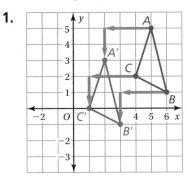

The coordinates
of the image are
$A'(2, 3)$, $B'(3, -1)$,
and $C'(1, 0)$.

Application Example

2. You map your neighborhood in a
coordinate plane. You walk from your
house at $(2, 1)$ to your school at $(5, 7)$.
Describe a possible translation on the
map for this situation.

⋮⋮ You can walk $5 - 2 = 3$ units right
and then $7 - 1 = 6$ units up.

PRACTICE MAKES PURR-FECT®

Check your answers at BigIdeasMath.com. ▬

The vertices of a quadrilateral are $A(-3, 1)$, $B(-2, 3)$, $C(-1, 3)$, and $D(-1, 1)$.
Draw the figure and its image after the translation.

3. 1 unit left and 5 units down

4. $(x + 4, y - 3)$

5. $(x + 3, y + 1)$

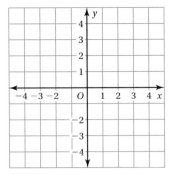

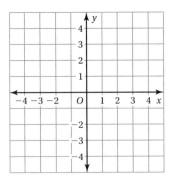

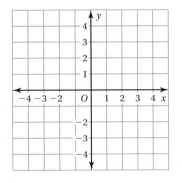

6. FLYING DISC You throw a flying disc to the point $(6, 4)$.
Use a translation to describe a path your friend can take
to catch the flying disc. _____

_____

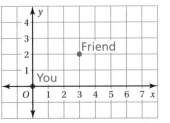

Key Concept and Vocabulary

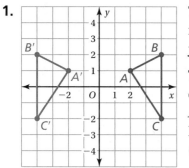

Line of reflection

Reflection

Flip

Visual Model

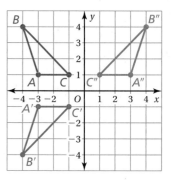

A reflection creates a mirror image of the original figure.

Skill Example

1.

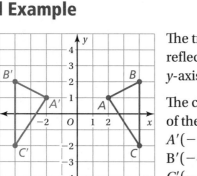

The triangle is reflected in the y-axis.

The coordinates of the image are $A'(-2, 1)$, $B'(-4, 2)$, and $C'(-4, -2)$.

Application Example

2. You design a logo using a triangle with vertices $P(0, 0)$, $Q(5, 2)$, and $R(3, 0)$. You reflect the figure in the x-axis to create the design. Draw the design in the coordinate plane.

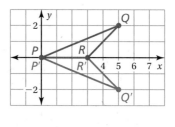

PRACTICE MAKES *PURR-FECT*®

Check your answers at BigIdeasMath.com.

Draw the figure and its reflection in the given axis.

3. $A(1, 4)$, $B(4, 3)$, $C(2, -3)$; y-axis

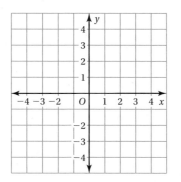

4. $P(-3, 3)$, $Q(4, 3)$, $R(3, 1)$, $S(0, 1)$; x-axis

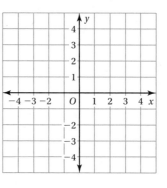

5. **LOGO** You design a logo using the figure shown. The entire logo is a reflection in both the x-axis and in the y-axis. Draw the rest of the logo in the coordinate plane.

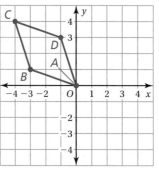

REVIEW: Rotations

Name _____

Key Concept and Vocabulary

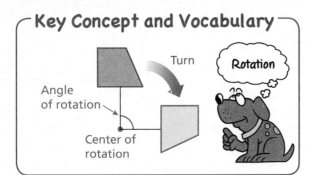

Visual Model

You can use coordinate rules for counterclockwise rotations about the origin.

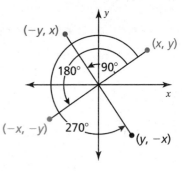

Skill Example

1.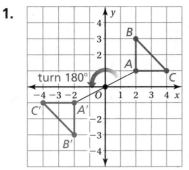

turn 180°

The coordinates of the image are
$A'(-2, -1)$, $B'(-2, -3)$, and $C'(-4, -1)$.

Application Example

2. Your location on a carnival ride is represented by the point (2, 6) in a coordinate plane. At the end of the ride, your location has rotated 90° counterclockwise about the origin. What is your new location?

$$(x, y) \longrightarrow (-y, x)$$
$$(2, 6) \longrightarrow (-6, 2)$$

⋰ Your new location is at $(-6, 2)$.

PRACTICE MAKES PURR-FECT®

Check your answers at BigIdeasMath.com.

The vertices of a triangle are $A(2, 0)$, $B(3, 1)$, and $C(4, -2)$. Draw the figure and its image after the rotation about the origin.

3. 270° counterclockwise

4. 180°

5. 270° clockwise

6. **SPINNER** A game spinner is shown in the coordinate plane. What coordinates do the spinner point to after a rotation of 90° clockwise about the origin?

_____

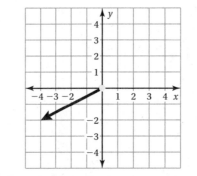

REVIEW: Dilations

Key Concept and Vocabulary

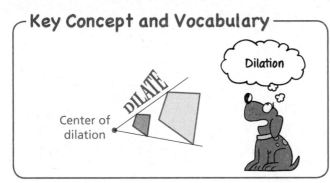

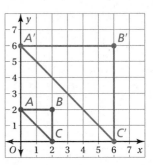

Center of dilation

Visual Model

To dilate with respect to the origin, multiply the coordinates of each vertex by the scale factor k.

Skill Example

1.

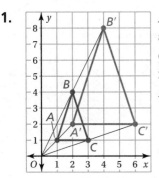

After a dilation with a scale factor of 2, the coordinates of the image are $A'(2, 2)$, $B'(4, 8)$, and $C'(6, 2)$.

Application Example

2. The location of a building is represented by the points $A(0, 0)$, $B(0, 4)$, $C(8, 4)$, and $D(8, 0)$ in a coordinate plane. An expansion of the building is represented using a dilation with a scale factor of 1.5. What are the coordinates of the image?

$$(x, y) \longrightarrow (1.5x, 1.5y)$$

❖ The coordinates of the image are $A'(0, 0)$, $B'(0, 6)$, $C'(12, 6)$, and $D'(12, 0)$.

PRACTICE MAKES PURR-FECT®

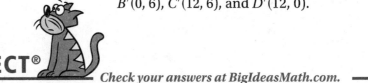

Check your answers at BigIdeasMath.com. ▬

Draw the figure and its image after a dilation with the given scale factor.

3. $A(1, 0)$, $B(1, 2)$, $C(2, 1)$; $k = 3$

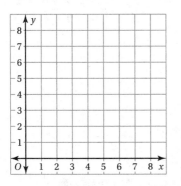

4. $P(-4, -4)$, $Q(-4, 2)$, $R(0, 2)$, $S(4, -4)$; $k = \dfrac{1}{2}$

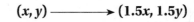

5. RESTAURANT A restaurant expands a patio using a dilation with a scale factor of 1.75. The dilated patio is represented in the coordinate plane. What were the coordinates of the original patio?

_____

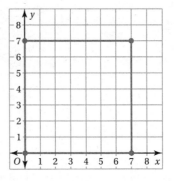

REVIEW: Similar Figures

Name _____

Key Concept and Vocabulary

Similar figures are the same shape, but not necessarily the same size.

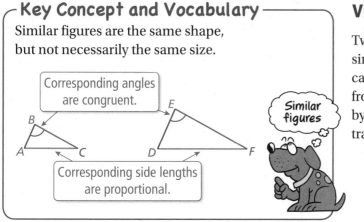

Corresponding angles are congruent.

Corresponding side lengths are proportional.

Similar figures

Visual Model

Two figures are similar when one can be obtained from the other by a similarity transformation.

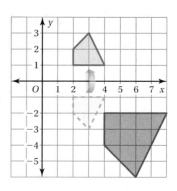

Skill Example

1.

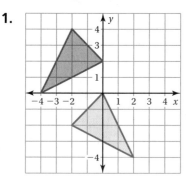

A similarity transformation is to rotate the red figure 90° counterclockwise about the origin, and then translate the image 2 units to the right.

Application Example

2. The flags are similar. How long is the smaller flag?

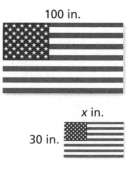

100 in.

60 in.

$$\frac{60}{30} = \frac{100}{x}$$

$$x = 50$$

⁙ The smaller flag is 50 inches long.

x in.

30 in.

PRACTICE MAKES *PURR-FECT*®

Check your answers at BigIdeasMath.com. ▬

Decide whether the two figures are similar.

3. Triangle A: $(1, 4), (3, 5), (4, 2)$

   Triangle B: $(0, 5), (4, 7), (6, 1)$

   _____

4. Quadrilateral A: $(-4, -2), (-2, 2), (2, -4), (-2, -4)$

   Quadrilateral B: $(2, 2), (1, -1), (-1, 3), (1, 3)$

   _____

5. **TENNIS COURTS** Are the two tennis courts similar? Explain. _____

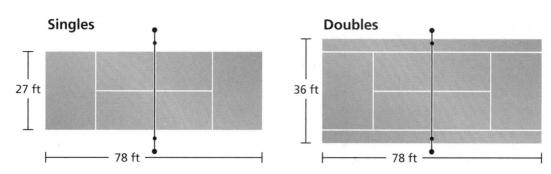

Singles

27 ft

78 ft

Doubles

36 ft

78 ft

6. **TENNIS COURTS** A scale model of the doubles tennis court is 0.52 foot long. What is the width of the model? _____

Name _____

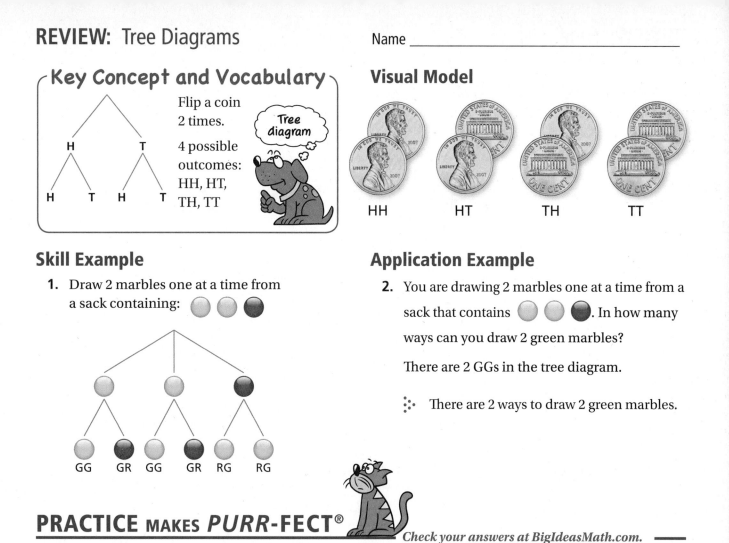

Key Concept and Vocabulary

Flip a coin 2 times.

Tree diagram

4 possible outcomes: HH, HT, TH, TT

Visual Model

HH   HT   TH   TT

Skill Example

1. Draw 2 marbles one at a time from a sack containing:

GG GR GG GR RG RG

Application Example

2. You are drawing 2 marbles one at a time from a sack that contains ⚪⚪⚫. In how many ways can you draw 2 green marbles?

There are 2 GGs in the tree diagram.

∴ There are 2 ways to draw 2 green marbles.

PRACTICE MAKES *PURR*-FECT®

Check your answers at BigIdeasMath.com.

Draw a tree diagram to show all the outcomes.

3. Flip a coin 3 times.

4. Draw 2 marbles one at a time from a sack with ⚪⚫ ⚪⚪.

5. You flip a coin 3 times. In how many ways can you get 2 heads and 1 tail? _____

6. You draw 2 marbles one at a time from a sack with ⚪⚫ ⚪⚪. In how many ways can you draw 2 green marbles? _____

7. **CARDS** You draw 2 cards one at a time from the hand at the right. In how many ways can you end up with a sum of 5? *(For instance, A + 4 = 5.)* _____

_____

REVIEW: Fundamental Counting Principle

Key Concept and Vocabulary

Event 1 can occur in m ways.

Event 2 can occur in n ways.

Event 1 followed by Event 2 can occur in $m \times n$ ways.

Counting principle

Multiply.

Visual Model

4 flavor choices for 1st scoop
4 flavor choices for 2nd scoop

$4 \times 4 = 16$ "two-scoop" cones

Skill Example

1. Event 1 can occur in 6 ways.
   Event 2 can occur in 3 ways.

   Event 1 followed by Event 2 can occur in

   $6 \times 3 = 18$ ways.

Application Example

2. How many outfits can you make using 3 T-shirts and 4 pairs of jeans?

   $3 \times 4 = 12$ outfits

   T-shirts   jeans

   ∴ You can make 12 different outfits.

PRACTICE MAKES PURR-FECT®

Check your answers at BigIdeasMath.com.

Find the number of ways that Event 1 can occur followed by Event 2.

3. Event 1 can occur in 5 ways.
   Event 2 can occur in 6 ways.

   _____

4. Event 1 can occur in 10 ways.
   Event 2 can occur in 3 ways.

   _____

5. Event 1 can occur in 11 ways.
   Event 2 can occur in 11 ways.

   _____

6. Event 1 can occur in 14 ways.
   Event 2 can occur in 4 ways.

   _____

Find the number of ways that Event 1 can occur followed by Event 2, followed by Event 3.

7. Event 1 can occur in 2 ways.
   Event 2 can occur in 4 ways.
   Event 3 can occur in 5 ways.

   _____

8. Event 1 can occur in 8 ways.
   Event 2 can occur in 7 ways.
   Event 3 can occur in 6 ways.

   _____

9. **OUTFITS** How many different outfits can you make using the T-shirts and jeans shown at the right? _____

10. **OUTFITS** How many of the outfits have the gray jeans? _____

REVIEW: Sample Space

Name _____

Key Concept and Vocabulary

The set of all outcomes of an experiment is called the **sample space**.

The sum of the probabilities of all outcomes in a sample space is 1.

Outcomes

Visual Model

A hat contains 3 tiles with the letters P, R, and O.

Experiment: Draw a tile.

Sample Space: P R O

Probabilities: $\frac{1}{3}$ $\frac{1}{3}$ $\frac{1}{3}$

Sum of Probabilities: $\frac{1}{3} + \frac{1}{3} + \frac{1}{3} = 1$

Skill Examples

1. You flip a coin. The sample space of the experiment is Heads (H), Tails (T).

2. You roll a number cube. The sample space of the experiment is 1, 2, 3, 4, 5, 6.

3. You flip a coin and roll a number cube. The sample space of the experiment is H1, H2, H3, H4, H5, H6, T1, T2, T3, T4, T5, T6.

Application Example

4. A referee flips a coin twice. Find the sample space. Show that the sum of the probabilities of all outcomes is 1.

   The sample space is HH, HT, TH, TT.

   The probability of each outcome is $\frac{1}{4}$.

   $$\frac{1}{4} + \frac{1}{4} + \frac{1}{4} + \frac{1}{4} = 1$$

PRACTICE MAKES *PURR-FECT*®

Check your answers at BigIdeasMath.com.

Find the sample space of the experiment.

5. Drawing a marble

   _____

6. Rolling a cube with letters of the word *sample*

   _____

7. Rolling a number cube twice

   _____

   _____

   _____

8. Flipping a coin and rolling the cube in Exercise 6

   _____

   _____

9. **BILLIARDS** The three balls shown are left on a billiards table. You choose a ball at random, set it aside, and then choose another ball. Find the sample space. Show that the sum of the probabilities of all outcomes is 1.

   _____

   _____

Credits